The Structure of Molecules

THE GENERAL CHEMISTRY MONOGRAPH SERIES

Russell Johnsen, Editor
Florida State University

Gordon M. Barrow (*Case Institute of Technology*)

THE STRUCTURE OF MOLECULES

Werner Herz (*Florida State University*)

THE SHAPE OF CARBON COMPOUNDS

Edward L. King (*University of Colorado*)

HOW CHEMICAL REACTIONS OCCUR

Bruce H. Mahan (*University of California, Berkeley*)

ELEMENTARY CHEMICAL THERMODYNAMICS

The Structure of Molecules

An Introduction to Molecular Spectroscopy

Gordon M. Barrow

Case Institute of Technology

1963

W. A. BENJAMIN, INC.   New York   Amsterdam

THE STRUCTURE OF MOLECULES
An Introduction to Molecular Spectroscopy

*Final manuscript was put into production on November 14, 1962;
the volume was published on May 15, 1963.*

*The publisher is pleased to acknowledge the
assistance of Galen Fleck, who edited
the manuscript, and William Prokos, who
produced the illustrations.*

W. A. BENJAMIN, INC.
2465 Broadway, New York 25, New York

Editor's Foreword

The teaching of general chemistry to beginning students becomes each day a more challenging and rewarding task as subject matter becomes more diverse and more complex and as the high school preparation of the student improves. These challenges have evoked a number of responses; this series of monographs for general chemistry is one such response. It is an experiment in the teaching of chemistry which recognizes a number of the problems that plague those who select textbooks and teach chemistry. First, it recognizes that no single book can physically encompass all the various aspects of chemistry that all instructors collectively deem important. Second, it recognizes that no single author is capable of writing authoritatively on all the topics that are included in everybody's list of what constitutes general chemistry. Finally, it recognizes the instructor's right to choose those topics that he considers to be important without having to apologize for having omitted large parts of an extensive textbook.

This volume, then, is one of approximately fifteen in the General Chemistry Monograph Series, each written by one or more highly qualified persons very familiar with the current status of the subject by virtue of research in it and also conversant with the problems associated with teaching the subject matter to beginning students. Each volume deals broadly with one of the subdivisions of general chemistry and constitutes a complete entity, far more comprehensive in its coverage than is permitted by the limitation of the standard one-volume text. Taken together, these volumes provide a range of topics from which the individual instructor can easily select those that will provide for his class an appropriate coverage of the material he considers most important.

Furthermore, inclusion of a number of topics that have only recently been considered for general chemistry courses, such as thermodynamics, molecular spectroscopy, and biochemistry, is planned, and these volumes will soon be available. In every instance a modern structural point of view has been adopted with the emphasis on general principles and unifying theory.

These volumes will have other uses also: selected monographs can be used to enrich the more conventional course of study by providing readily available, inexpensive supplements to standard texts. They should also prove valuable to students in other areas of the physical and biological sciences needing supplementary information in any field of chemistry pertinent to their own special interests. Thus, students of biology will find the monographs on biochemistry, organic chemistry, and reaction kinetics particularly useful. Beginning students in physics and meteorology will find the monograph on thermodynamics rewarding. Teachers of elementary science will also find these volumes invaluable aids to bringing them up to date in the various branches of chemistry.

Each monograph has several features which make it especially useful as an aid to teaching. These include a large number of solved examples and problems for the student, a glossary of technical terms, and copious illustrations.

The authors of the several monographs deserve much credit for their enthusiasm which made this experiment possible. Professor Rolfe Herber of Rutgers University has been of invaluable assistance in the preparation of this series, having supplied editorial comment and numerous valuable suggestions on each volume. Thanks are also due to Professor M. Kasha of the Florida State University for many suggestions during the planning stages and for reading several of the manuscripts.

RUSSELL JOHNSEN

Tallahassee, Florida
October 1962

Preface

It is increasingly important for the student of general chemistry to be able to interpret chemical and physical phenomena in terms of molecular behavior. It follows that he must learn as much as he can about the nature and behavior of individual molecules.

One basic way of determining the "physical" properties of molecules is the measurement of the radiation they emit or absorb. This is spectroscopy, and I have attempted here to provide an introduction to the subject.

The methods by which information is deduced from spectroscopy are described and applied to some relatively simple cases. Although the spectroscopic analysis of more complicated systems demands a mathematical approach, an understanding of the principles and scope of the technique does not. This book shows how the properties of molecules can be gained from spectra, and in so doing provides an extension to the introductory study of chemistry.

As the student's interest in spectroscopy grows and, when he has acquired an additional background in mathematics and physics, he will want to turn to more advanced works on the subject. A selection of these is given in the following list:

G. M. Barrow, *Introduction to Molecular Spectroscopy*, McGraw-Hill, New York, 1962

R. P. Bauman, *Absorption Spectroscopy*, Wiley, New York, 1962

G. H. Beaven, E. A. Johnson, H. A. Willis, and R. G. T. Miller, *Molecular Spectroscopy: Methods and Applications in Chemistry*, Macmillan, New York, 1961

vii

W. Brügel, *An Introduction to Infrared Spectroscopy*, Wiley, New
    York, 1962
R. E. Dodd, *Chemical Spectroscopy*, Elsevier, New York, 1962

GORDON M. BARROW

Cleveland, Ohio
January 1963

Contents

Editor's Foreword   v

Preface   vii

Introduction   1

I Radiation and the Energies of Molecules   3

  1–1 Nature of Radiation   4
  1–2 Introduction to the Methods of Measuring the Absorption of Radiation   11
  1–3 Energy of Molecules   15
  1–4 Quantum Restrictions on Molecular Energies   21
  1–5 Boltzmann Distribution   24
  1–6 Types of Molecular Spectroscopy   26
  Summary   26
    Exercises   27

II Rotational Spectra and the Size and Shape of Molecules   29

  2–1 Observational Methods for the Absorption of Radiation by Rotating Molecules   30
  2–2 Rotation of Ordinary-Sized Objects   32
  2–3 Quantum Restrictions—Rotation of Diatomic Molecules   37

2–4   Rotational Spectra and Bond Lengths of Diatomic Molecules   40
2–5   Interaction of Radiation with Rotating Molecules   46
2–6   Extension of the Method to Other Molecules   48
2–7   Extensions and Subtleties   54
Summary   55
  Exercises   57

III   Vibrational Spectra and the Flexibility of Molecules   59

3–1   Experimental Methods in Infrared Spectral Region   60
3–2   Vibration of Ball-and-Spring Systems   62
3–3   Vibrational Energies of Diatomic Molecules   68
3–4   Vibrational Spectra and Force Constants of Diatomic Molecules   71
3–5   Amplitude of Molecular Vibrations   74
3–6   Mechanism of Infrared-Radiation Absorption   75
3–7   Vibrational Spectra of Polyatomic Molecules   77
3–8   Potential-Energy Function for a Chemical Bond   82
Summary   85
  Exercises   86

IV   The Simultaneous Rotation and Vibration of Diatomic Molecules   89

4–1   Energies of Vibrating and Rotating Molecules   89
4–2   Rotation-Vibration Spectrum of Gaseous Diatomic Molecules   91
4–3   Relative Component Intensities of a Rotation-Vibration Absorption Band   96
4–4   Asymmetry of a Rotation-Vibration Absorption Band   99
Summary   105
  Exercises   105

V   Spectra Due to Change in the Arrangement of the Electrons of a Molecule   107

5–1   Diatomic-Molecular Energies in Different Electronic Arrangements   108

5–2   Electronic Transitions—Effect of Vibrational-
          Energy Changes   111
5–3   Analysis of Rotational-Energy Changes Accom-
          panying Electronic and Vibrational Tran-
          sitions   115
5–4   Electronic Spectra of Larger Molecules   117
5–5   Electronic Spectra of Hydrocarbons with Double
          Bonds   118
5–6   Electronic Spectra Due to Nonbonding Electrons   123
5–7   Electronic Spectra of Metal Ions   126
5–8   Charge-Transfer Spectra   133
Summary   136
   Exercises   137

VI   **The Emission or Dissipation of Energy by Excited
         Molecules**   138

6–1   Nonradiative Energy-Transfer Processes   139
6–2   Fluorescent Emission of Radiation   144
6–3   Phosphorescent Emission of Radiation   148
Summary   150

Glossary: Symbols   152

Index   155

Constants

Symbol	Description	Value
c	Velocity of light	3.00×10^{10} cm/sec
h	Planck's constant	6.62×10^{-27} erg-sec
k	Boltzmann's constant	1.38×10^{-16} erg/deg-molecule
R	Gas constant	1.99 cal/deg-mole

Introduction

The chemist must learn to live in, and to feel at home in, the world of molecules. It is not enough that he knows the chemical constitution and chemical reactions of the materials around him. To be really effective and successful, he must also develop an intimacy with the molecular world. He must fit himself into the molecular scale of things. He must put that first drummed-in chemical fact that molecules are small in the very back of his mind and replace it by a consciousness that molecules are real, intricate, structural arrangements of atoms in space.

No study brings one more quickly to an intimacy with molecules, with their size, shape, flexibility, and so forth, than does spectroscopy. The methods of spectroscopy almost let one "see" individual molecules. The brief account of molecular spectroscopy that follows will, for example, show that we can determine that the bond length of the HF molecule is 0.917×10^{-8} cm (or 0.361×10^{-8} in.) and that that of HCl is 1.275×10^{-8} cm. Furthermore, it will be seen that it is almost exactly twice as difficult to stretch the bond of the HF molecule—by, say, 10 per cent—as it is to do the same to the HCl molecule.

An appreciation that such molecular properties can be measured —and therefore that one can, in a way, see the details of individual

I

molecules—brings one quickly and directly to a "feeling" for the world of molecules. With this philosophy the student can bring to bear on all later studies of chemistry, or biochemistry, the questions that the modern chemist asks: What does this reaction (or rate, or property, etc.) tell me about the behavior of the molecules of the system? How can I understand this reaction, etc., in terms of the known behavior of the molecules of the system?

Although the methods of spectroscopy will be dealt with here primarily in terms of the study of the properties of individual molecules, it must be mentioned that these methods find a wide and ever-increasing use for the identification and analysis of all types of chemical systems. The material to be presented here will provide the background that allows one to understand such practical applications of spectroscopy. The absorption of radiation in the infrared spectral region, for example, turns out to be remarkably characteristic of the molecules of the absorbing material. One can, therefore, use the infrared absorption spectrum of a compound to characterize the compound or to analyze for this compound in a mixture. While such applications can be made without a knowledge of what is happening when the molecules absorb radiation, full use of these techniques in a satisfying way requires the understanding of the molecular basis of spectroscopy that will be reached by a study of this monograph.

I

Radiation and
the Energies of Molecules

To begin with, it is perhaps desirable to emphasize that the methods used to find out about molecules by spectroscopy are, to some extent, similar to the procedure of looking at ordinary-sized objects to determine their sizes and shapes. In spectroscopy we "look at" the molecules of a sample by shining light through the sample and measuring, by a suitable instrument, which wavelengths of the light have been absorbed by the molecules of the sample. The material of the following chapters will show that the radiation absorbed by a sample reveals many of the properties of the molecules of the sample. The measurement of the absorption of radiation by a sample, or of the emission of radiation by a hot sample, and the deduction of the properties of the molecules of the sample from these measurements constitutes molecular spectroscopy. The methods of spectroscopy can be adequately illustrated by restricting the treatment to small molecules, and primarily to diatomic molecules. It will be made clear, however, that the principles established here can be extended, with some added complexities, to larger molecules.

Before studying spectra in detail it is necessary to go over some of the general features of the topics which, when combined, will re-

veal the molecular sizes and shapes in which we are interested. The
principal basic topics that will now be introduced are the nature of
radiation, the experimental methods available for studying the
absorption of radiation, and some of the general features of the
energies of individual molecules.

1–1   NATURE OF RADIATION

Here we must talk about the nature of a beam of light so that
later we can understand the way in which such a beam interacts
with the molecules that are placed in its path. Two rather different
descriptions of a light beam are used in spectroscopy. These two
views of the nature of a light beam stem from the early, and then
opposing, wave and corpuscular theories of the nature of light.

Wave Nature of Radiation

The wave-nature view of radiation is usually adopted, for example, when one considers phenomena such as the spreading out of
white, i.e., "ordinary," light into its color components as a result
of passage through a prism. The process is indicated in Fig. 1–1.
In this description of radiation the waves consist of electric and

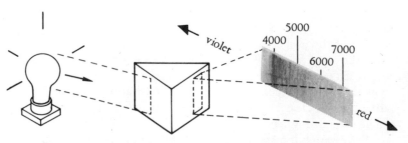

Figure 1–1 The spreading out of a beam of white light by
means of a prism.

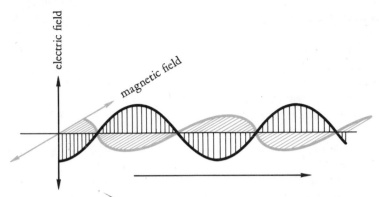

Figure 1–2 A beam of radiation according to the wave-
nature picture. Each wave crest moves with the velocity of
light in the direction of the beam. (Only one component of
the electric and magnetic fields has been shown; i.e., plane-
polarized light is shown.)

magnetic fields which, as Fig. 1–2 illustrates, move in the direction
of the beam of radiation in a manner similar to that of waves moving
along the surface of water. When light is described in terms of these
waves, the effect of a prism in the light beam is said to be that of
spreading out the original beam according to the wavelengths of the
electric and magnetic fields which constitute the beam. Passage
through the prism generally bends the short-wavelength components of the light beam to a greater extent than it does the longer-
wavelength components. A wavelength scale as well as a color scale
can, therefore, be attached to the spectrum, illustrated in Fig. 1–1,
that results from the passage of light through a prism.

The electrical and magnetic effects that are associated with the
waves shown in Fig. 1–2 need not be studied here. It can be mentioned, however, that it is the electric rather than the magnetic
field that is important in spectroscopic studies. Furthermore, we
can point out that an electric field is said to exist if a charged particle, say an electron, feels a force pushing it one way or the other.
Thus an electron in the path of the beam shown in Fig. 1–2 would
experience a force acting to push it up for one-half of a wave cycle
and a force acting to push it down for the other half of the cycle.

As the wave passed by, therefore, the electron would repeatedly feel these pushes and pulls.

The wave-nature interpretation of radiation, therefore, describes radiation as consisting of electric and magnetic fields that travel in the direction of the beam with a speed of about 3×10^{10} cm/sec. The waves that constitute the radiation can have various wavelengths; and, as shown by the effect of a prism on visible radiation, the radiation can be spread out according to its wavelength.

In addition to describing radiation in terms of the length of the waves that constitute the radiation, one can, as for any wave motion, also characterize the wave motion by a frequency. The relation between the wavelength and the frequency of a traveling wave is best revealed by considering, as illustrated in Fig. 1–3, a source of waves and an observer stationed a certain distance away from the source. If the speed with which the waves travel is denoted by c cm/sec, it is convenient, mathematically, to have the observer stationed a distance c *cm* from the source. Then a particular wave crest that leaves the source will reach the observer in 1 sec. The observer will see the maxima and minima of the waves moving by him, and he would be likely to characterize the wave by the number of

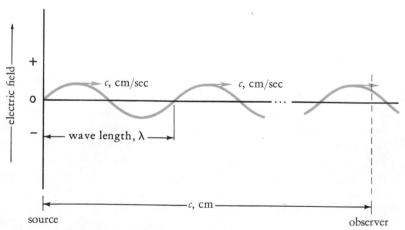

Figure 1–3   Diagram for the derivation $\nu = c/\lambda$.

cycles that passed by him per unit time, say per second. If he did so, he would, in a 1-sec time interval, see all the waves pass by him that were on their way to him between the source and his position at the beginning of the 1-sec interval. Since he is at a distance equal to c, the speed of the waves, away from the source and since, as Fig. 1–3 shows, the length of one wave is denoted by λ, the number of waves between the source and the observer is c/λ. This quantity measures the number of waves or cycles that would pass by the observer each second, and it is therefore the frequency of the wave. If ν is introduced to represent the frequency in cycles per second, we can write the relation, often used in spectroscopic work,

$$\nu = \frac{c}{\lambda}. \tag{1}$$

(It might be mentioned that a molecule in a beam of radiation is rather like the observer in the above derivation. The molecule experiences the effect of the electric field pointing one way and then the other. This back-and-forth effect occurs with the frequency that, as we have seen, is given by c/λ.)

To illustrate the values that occur for λ and ν, we can consider the radiation that appears red. Such radiation has a wavelength of about 7×10^{-5} cm, or, in the often-used units of angstroms (1 cm $= 10^8$ A), 7000 A. The corresponding frequency is

$$\nu = \frac{c}{\lambda} = \frac{3 \times 10^{10} \text{ cm/sec}}{7 \times 10^{-5} \text{ cm}} = 4.3 \times 10^{14} \text{ cycles/sec.}$$

At the other end of the visible spectrum is violet light, which has a wavelength of about 4500 A, or 4.5×10^{-5} cm. Its frequency is calculated to be

$$\nu = \frac{3 \times 10^{10}}{4.5 \times 10^{-5}} = 6.7 \times 10^{14} \text{ cycles/sec.}$$

The inconveniently large numerical values that are often encountered, as the above examples illustrate, when the frequency of radiation is dealt with have led spectroscopists to introduce a quantity that is proportional to the frequency ν but differs from it by a proportionality factor. Fairly convenient quantities are obtained by defining a quantity $\bar{\nu}$ simply as

$$\bar{\nu} = \frac{1}{\lambda}. \tag{2}$$

One sees that the values of $\bar{\nu}$ will be smaller than those for ν, defined as c/λ, by the factor of c. For red light one has, for example,

$$\bar{\nu} = \frac{1}{7 \times 10^{-5} \text{ cm}} = 14{,}000 \text{ cm}^{-1}.$$

It is important to remember that both ν and $\bar{\nu}$ are measures of the frequency of the radiation. In fact, one often talks of $\bar{\nu}$ as a frequency. One should note that conversion of λ to $\bar{\nu}$ can be made, if λ is expressed in centimeters, by the reciprocal relation of Eq. (2). It is this simple tie to λ that has led to use of the term "wave number" for $\bar{\nu}$. Thus one might say that red light has a wave number of about 14,000 reciprocal centimeters, or centimeters^{-1}.

Quantum Nature of Radiation

Another approach to the description of the nature of a beam of radiation is sometimes more convenient. A number of experimental situations suggest the concept that radiation consists of a stream of energy packets, called photons or quanta, which travel in the direction of the beam with the velocity of light. For example, the experiments in which light falls on a metal and ejects electrons, as occurs in a phototube, were shown by Einstein to be understandable on the basis of this quantum picture of light. This interpretation of the nature of radiation as a stream of energy packets is also convenient when we are concerned with the absorption of the radiation by molecules in a sample through which the beam passes. A molecule may, as we shall see, absorb or emit one of these quanta and thereby increase or decrease its energy.

Planck's Relation and the Electromagnetic Spectrum

The two different ways of looking at the nature of light, although apparently antagonistic, are, in fact, closely related. This was first realized as a result of the investigations of Max Planck around the turn of the century. It was finally recognized that both views were "correct" and that they differed because they described different facets of the behavior of radiation. The basic relation that allows one to go from one approach to the other, a procedure often necessary in spectroscopy, is

$$\Delta\epsilon = h\nu, \tag{3}$$

where h, the proportionality constant between $\Delta\epsilon$, the energy of a quantum, and ν, the frequency of the wave motion, is known as Planck's constant. It has the value 6.62×10^{-27} erg-sec.

The Planck relation allows a beam of monochromatic radiation, i.e., a beam with a given wavelength or frequency, to be interpreted also as a stream of quanta of a given energy. A beam with a different wavelength or frequency will correspond to a stream of quanta with a different energy. The Planck relation allows one to convert, quantitatively, from the concept that the radiation is a wave to the concept that it is a stream of quanta.

Let us illustrate Eq. (3) with an example. Radiation that appears red and has a wavelength λ of 7000 A can again be used. The energy of a single quantum of this radiation can be calculated according to Planck's relation as

$$\begin{aligned}
\Delta\epsilon &= h\nu \\
&= (6.62 \times 10^{-27})(4.3 \times 10^{14}) \\
&= 2.85 \times 10^{-12} \text{ erg.}
\end{aligned}$$

The energy of a single quantum of radiation is, of course, very small. We shall see later, however, that the energy of a single quantum of radiation can, depending on the value of ν or λ, be quite appreciable compared with the energy of an individual molecule. The absorption of a quantum of radiation can, as we shall see, make a molecule rotate faster or vibrate faster or can even break a bond of the molecule.

Some idea of the values of λ, ν, $\bar{\nu}$, and $\Delta\epsilon$ that are encountered in spectroscopic studies can be gained from study of Fig. 1–4. The regions labeled as microwave, infrared, visible, and ultraviolet are so labeled primarily, as is most obvious for the visible region, because of the range and type of instruments that are available for studying the radiation. Further comments will be made regarding

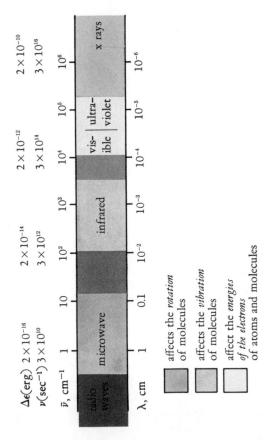

$\Delta\epsilon(\text{erg})$ 2×10^{-16} $\qquad$ 2×10^{-14} $\qquad$ 2×10^{-12} $\qquad$ 2×10^{-10}
$\nu(\text{sec}^{-1})$ 3×10^{10} $\qquad$ 3×10^{12} $\qquad$ 3×10^{14} $\qquad$ 3×10^{16}

$\bar{\nu}$, cm^{-1} 1 $\qquad$ 10 $\qquad$ 10^2 $\qquad$ 10^3 $\qquad$ 10^4 $\qquad$ 10^5 $\qquad$ 10^6

| radio waves | microwave | | infrared | | vis-ible | ultra-violet | x rays |

λ, cm   1   0.1 10^{-2} 10^{-3} 10^{-4} 10^{-5} 10^{-6}

affects the *rotation* of molecules

affects the *vibration* of molecules

affect the *energies of the electrons* of atoms and molecules

Figure 1-4 The regions of electromagnetic radiation.

IO

the experimental methods used in various wavelength regions in the following section. It will, however, be helpful to keep in mind the general features of Fig. 1-4, that is, that the microwave region is that in which the radiation has low-energy quanta, long wavelengths, and so forth, and that the visible region is bounded by the infrared region on the low-quantum-energy, long-wavelength side and by the ultraviolet region on the high-quantum-energy, short-wavelength side, and so forth.

1-2 INTRODUCTION TO THE METHODS OF MEASURING THE ABSORPTION OF RADIATION

Many experimental methods are available for studying the absorption or emission of radiation by molecules. The variety of methods is dictated by the fact that various components needed in these spectroscopic studies are effective only for radiation in certain regions of the entire range of radiation. Thus the eye is sensitive, i.e., serves as a detector of radiation, only for radiation with wavelengths between about 4500 and 7000 A. For this "experimental" reason we call this region of electromagnetic radiation the visible region. In a similar manner various materials serve as efficient emitters or detectors or as transparent materials in the other regions, and the experimental methods in the different regions depend on the nature of these materials and components.

Perhaps the simplest device that can be constructed for studying spectra is the spectroscope illustrated in Fig. 1-5a. (One uses the term "spectroscope" if the radiation is detected with the eye. If a photographic plate is used to detect the radiation, the term spectrograph is appropriate. If, as now is often the case, some type of phototube or other electronic detector is used, the instrument may be referred to as a spectrophotometer. Perhaps more convenient, however, for the many instruments that have detectors that give a signal which can be electrically amplified and presented as a recording on chart paper is the term "spectrometer.") The simple spectroscope, arranged as in Fig. 1-5a for studying absorption spectra, is adequate to illustrate the three principal components of any spectrometer and also to illustrate the experimental procedure for measuring the radiation absorbed by the molecules of the sample.

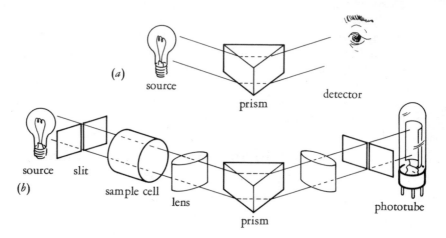

Figure 1–5   **A simple visible spectroscope (*a*) and spectrometer (*b*) illustrating the basic components.**

The three basic components of almost any spectrometer are the source of radiation; a unit which spreads out, or disperses, the radiation according to its wavelength; and a device which can detect the amount of radiation of various wavelengths that passes from the source through the sample and the dispersing unit. In addition, it should be mentioned, there must be an entrance slit to give a well-defined beam, a collimating lens to make the beam parallel before it enters the prism, a focusing lens to bring the various wavelengths of radiation to a focus after the beam passes through the prism, and an exit slit that can be moved along an axis perpendicular to the emerging beam so that the radiation of various wavelengths can be looked at. All these additional units are illustrated in the more detailed diagram of a visible spectrometer shown in Fig. 1–5*b*.

The way in which the absorption spectrum of a sample that absorbs in the visible region, i.e., a colored sample, might be obtained is illustrated in Fig. 1–6. First one would measure the amount of radiation that the source—an ordinary tungsten electric light bulb is suitable—produces with no sample present in the sample cell. The amount would vary somewhat with wavelength, and

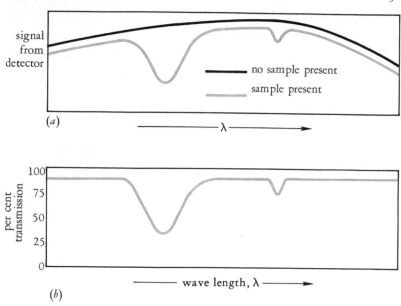

signal
from
detector

no sample present
sample present

(*a*)

λ

100

75

per cent
transmission

50

25

0

wave length, λ

(*b*)

Figure 1–6   Two ways of illustrating the amount of radiation absorbed by a sample.

one might obtain an output from the phototube that gave a curve like that shown by the black line in Fig. 1–6*a*. Next one would repeat the experiment but with the sample in the light beam. The sample would absorb the radiation in some regions, and now the photometer output might have the form shown by the red curve of Fig. 1–6*a*. The "absorption bands" of the sample are clearly noticeable in such a pair of traces. More often, however, one calculates the percentage of the radiation that has passed through the sample and converts the two curves to one showing the percentage of transmission. Such a curve is given in Fig. 1–6*b*. (When absorption of radiation occurs over a fairly broad range of wavelengths, one often refers to this absorption as an absorption band. In many experiments, as we will see, we obtain absorption over very narrow wavelength ranges—so narrow, in fact, that then one talks of absorption lines.)

Essentially the same experiment is performed to obtain the

absorption spectra of molecular samples in the microwave, the infrared, and the ultraviolet regions. Furthermore, the same instrumental components that were pointed out for the simple spectrometer that could be used in the visible region can be recognized. The principal changes in the components that are necessary in the various regions are summarized in Table 1–1.

Two features common to almost all presently used spectrometers that operate in the ultraviolet, visible, or infrared regions should perhaps be mentioned at this stage. As will be immediately noticed if a commercially available instrument is inspected, the radiation beam is interrupted by a rotating chopper. The effect of this is to produce, from the detector, a varying or a-c type of signal rather than the steady or d-c type of signal that would be produced without the chopper. There are a number of technical advantages that lead to use of chopped radiation. For example, the amplifier can be so tuned that it amplifies only signals that have the same frequency as does the chopper. In this way extraneous signals that the sensitive detector might pick up are not amplified.

The second general feature common to most spectrometers is that of double-beam operation. Instead of separately measuring the radiation that passes through the instrument and empty sample cell

Table 1–1
The Principal Components of Spectrometers
Used in the Various Spectral Regions

	Source	*Dispersing element*	*Detector*
Ultraviolet	H_2 discharge tube	Quartz prism or grating	Photomultiplier tube
Visible	Tungsten lamp	Glass prism or grating	Photomultiplier tube
Infrared	Heated ceramic element	Rock-salt prism or grating	Thermocouple
Microwave	Klystron tube		Quartz crystal

and then repeating the measurements with the sample present in the cell, arrangements are made so that the instrument directly compares the radiation that gets through the sample with that that gets through a reference cell. (If the sample were in the form of a solute in a solution, the reference cell would contain pure solvent.) Typically, two beams are taken from the source; one passes through the sample compartment and one through the reference compartment. These beams, perhaps chopped out of phase, are then optically combined and fall on the detector. The detector then sees the difference in the intensity of the two beams; and if only this a-c signal is amplified, the instrument gives directly a measure of the additional absorption that occurs in the sample cell.

As our discussion of spectroscopy proceeds, this general introduction will be supplemented by further mention of the special techniques and components that must be used to obtain spectra in the various spectral regions.

1–3   ENERGY OF MOLECULES

Before we proceed to "see" molecules by studying the radiation that they absorb, it will be helpful first to become generally familiar with the ways in which a molecule can store various energies. Although we shall also study molecules in the liquid state, let us first think about the energy of a molecule of a gas. It will be recalled that the molecules of a gas, at not too high pressures, are small compared with the volume occupied by the gas. Although the molecules occasionally collide with one another, they are for the most part moving freely through space. It is possible, therefore, to talk about the energy of an individual gas-phase molecule. We shall see, furthermore, that the energy of a molecule can be described, for the most part, in much the same way as we describe the energy of an ordinary-sized object. Thus we shall recognize an energy component due to the translational motion of the molecule; a component due to the rotation of the molecule about its center of gravity; a component due to the vibrations of the atoms of the molecule against one another; and, finally, an energy that is due to the arrangement, or the energy, of the electrons that are in the molecule.

It is true, however, that some special, very interesting features will be important because we shall be dealing with molecular rather than ordinary-sized phenomena.

Energy Due to
Translational Motion

We first recognize that any moving particle has kinetic energy as a result of its motion through space. This is known as *translational energy*. The student may already have dealt with this molecular motion in relating the pressure exerted by a gas to the collisions which the molecules of a gas make with the walls of the container. But now we ask, how fast do the molecules travel? Or, what is more to the point here, how much translational energy does a molecule have?

An answer can be given by seeing what the molecular velocities would have to be to lead to the observed pressure. The student has, perhaps, derived the necessary result in connection with his studies of the nature and behavior of gases. We shall not go through the derivation here. It is enough for our interest in molecular energies to report that the *average translational kinetic energy* of a single molecule in the x, the y, and the z directions is found to be equal to $\frac{1}{2}kT$, where k is a constant known as Boltzmann's constant and T is the temperature on the absolute scale. The constant k has the value 1.38×10^{-16} erg/deg. The total translational kinetic energy of a molecule is, therefore, $\frac{3}{2}kT$. The quantity kT, or $\frac{1}{2}kT$ or $\frac{3}{2}kT$, is, as we shall see, a very convenient reference amount with which all types of molecular energies can be compared. For a molecule at room temperature, about 25°C, one sees that its translational energy, if it is moving with an average speed, is

$$\tfrac{1}{2}kT = \tfrac{1}{2}(1.38 \times 10^{-16})(298) = 2.06 \times 10^{-14} \text{ erg}$$

for each of the three perpendicular directions in which it is free to move and that its total translational energy is

$$\tfrac{3}{2}kT = 6.2 \times 10^{-14} \text{ erg.}$$

These are, of course, average values, and many molecules will have much more and others much less than these amounts.

Although in spectroscopic studies we shall, as the above numbers suggest, often be concerned with the energy of individual
molecules, we shall also, at times, deal with the energy of a mole,
i.e., an Avogadro's number, of molecules. On this basis we would
introduce Avogadro's number and report the kinetic energies per
mole as $N(\frac{1}{2}kT) = \frac{1}{2}RT$ along a given direction or as $N(\frac{3}{2}kT) = \frac{3}{2}RT$
in space. The gas constant R, related to k by

$$R = Nk,$$

is convenient for describing energies of a mole. In fact, the gas
constant R and its value of 1.987 cal/mole/deg may be more familiar
to the chemist than is the Boltzmann constant k. They are simply
related, but one needs to note that one generally uses R in calorie
units whereas k is commonly used with the units of ergs. (One
might notice that Boltzmann's constant can be looked on as the gas
constant per molecule.) In molar quantities one would probably
report the kinetic energy due to the translational motion of the
molecules of a gas at 25°C as

$$\tfrac{3}{2}RT = \tfrac{3}{2}(1.987)(298) = 890 \text{ cal/mole/deg}.$$

The fact that a molecule is free to move in the three perpendicular, or orthogonal, directions x, y, and z and that energies due
to motion in these directions add together to give the total energy
suggest the introduction of the idea of *degrees of freedom* to describe
the ways in which a molecule can move and, therefore, have energy.
We say that there are three translational degrees of freedom and
that each contributes a kinetic energy of $\frac{1}{2}kT$ to the molecule. These
translational degrees of freedom are represented, along with other
degrees of freedom to be introduced, in Fig. 1–7.

Energy Due to
Rotational Motion

Let us now proceed to ask: How else can our freely moving
molecule have energy? By analogy with ordinary-sized systems we
must expect that it can rotate, or revolve, about an axis through its
center of gravity and, therefore, have *rotational energy*. If one thinks
of a football kicked through the air, one recognizes that it can

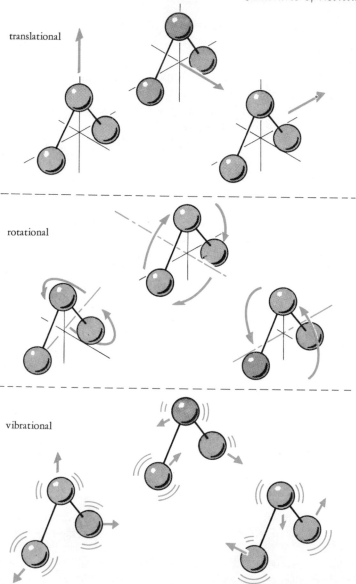

translational

rotational

vibrational

Figure 1–7   Three different ways in which molecules can store energy as a result of motion of the atoms of the molecule— illustrated by a nonlinear triatomic molecule.

rotate about its long axis (i.e., it can spiral) or it can rotate end over end. In fact, the second motion might occur in a vertical or a horizontal plane. As for this example, any generally shaped particle, including a molecule, can rotate about the three axes that pass through the center of gravity of the molecule and are mutually perpendicular. We say that a molecule has three rotational degrees of freedom.

The special case of rotation of a molecule in which the atoms lie in a line, i.e., a linear molecule, is comparable to the rotation of a length of wire. Only rotation about the two axes perpendicular to the length of the molecule, or the wire, constitute rotations of the system and for linear molecules we have, therefore, only two rotational degrees of freedom. All diatomic molecules are, of course, necessarily linear, and these will be molecules with which we will often deal in our study of molecular structure.

Experience with the translation motion of molecules might now lead us to expect an average rotational kinetic energy of $\frac{1}{2}kT$ for each of the three, or two, rotational degrees of freedom. Such an expectation is, as we will see, somewhat upset by the peculiarities that characterize some of the motions of molecular-sized particles.

Energy Due to
Vibrational Motion

A third way in which a molecule can acquire energy results from the vibrations of the molecule. It turns out to be remarkably satisfactory to treat a molecule as if the atoms of the molecule were point masses and as if the bonds holding the atoms together were springs. The molecule is not a rigid structure: it is flexible and is very much the counterpart of a set of balls held together by ordinary springs. Such flexible systems vibrate, and molecules will therefore have *vibrational energy*.

As in the preceding discussions of translational and rotational energies, we need to ask how many ways there are for a molecule containing n atoms to vibrate, i.e., how many vibrational degrees of freedom there are in a molecule containing n atoms. To answer this question, we consider a molecule and first count the total degrees of freedom that it would have if the bonds were imagined to be very weak. Then we would probably think of the n atoms of the molecule as being independent particles and for each particle we would think of translation in the three perpendicular directions and would ascribe 3 degrees of freedom to each atom. With this view, the collection of n atoms that constitute the molecule would have a total of $3n$ degrees of freedom.

Now let us imagine the bonds to be gradually strengthened until they are normal bonds. In this gradual, imagined process the number of degrees of freedom will not suddenly change. It follows that an actual molecule of n atoms has a total of $3n$ degrees of freedom. For a molecule, however, we do not like to ascribe 3 of these to the motion of each atom. Rather we ascribe 3, of the total of $3n$, to translational motion of the entire molecule as a unit and 3 (or 2 for linear molecules) to the rotation of the entire molecule. The remaining $3n - 6$ (or $3n - 5$ for linear molecules) must be accounted for by internal motions. These internal motions are vibrations, and we have therefore shown that a molecule with n atoms has $3n - 6$ (or $3n - 5$) vibrational degrees of freedom.

In Fig. 1–7 the three vibrations of a bent triatomic molecule are depicted, and these complete the set of $3n$ degrees of freedom illustrated there for the molecule. In a later chapter, when we shall deal in more detail with vibrations, we shall see that the number of vibrational degrees of freedom $3n - 6$ (or $3n - 5$) corresponds to the number of basic ways in which the molecule can vibrate.

Energy Due to the Electrons of the Molecule

One final, rather different type of molecular energy will be of interest. The three molecular energy types treated so far can be based on a rather mechanical model of the molecule that ignores the detailed structure of the molecule in terms of nuclei and electrons. It is possible, however, for the energy of a molecule to change as a result of a change in the energy of the electrons of which it is composed. In this way we come to the fourth and final molecular energy type: *electronic energy*. One can think of changes in the electronic energy of a molecule as being due to an increase in the kinetic, and potential, energy of one of the electrons of the molecule. It is not customary to assign a number of degrees of freedom to electronic energy. Strictly speaking, there would, of course, be 3 times the number of electrons. In practice it is enough to know that a molecule can sometimes change to a state of higher energy as a result of one of its electrons gaining energy.

Thus, the four types of molecular energy, translational, rotational, vibrational, and electronic, have been introduced. So far, however, nothing about these energies that is peculiar to molecular systems—and these peculiarities are very important in molecular spectroscopy—has been discussed. Let us now introduce these peculiarities.

1-4 QUANTUM RESTRICTIONS ON MOLECULAR ENERGIES

What is it about molecular energies that allows a study of these energies, by means of the way in which energy is absorbed from a beam of radiation, to reveal the details of molecular structure?

First it must just be stated that the energy of a particle which is confined to movement in a very small region (one of molecular dimensions) is restricted to certain values; i.e., only certain energies are allowed. For example, a rotating molecule cannot rotate with any velocity and rotational energy. This motion is subject to what are called *quantum restrictions* which allow the molecule to have only certain velocities and energies. The CO molecule, for example, can have rotational energies of 0, 7.6×10^{-16}, 22.9×10^{-16}, 45.8×10^{-16}, . . . erg/molecule, which correspond to rotational velocities of 0, 1.6×10^{11}, 2.8×10^{11}, 4.0×10^{11}, . . . revolutions/sec. Intermediate values are not allowed.

The energies that are allowed for a particular type of motion for a particular molecule are often represented by a diagram with horizontal lines on a vertical energy scale, as illustrated in Fig. 1-8*b*. There is no abscissa scale on such diagrams, and the length of the lines has no significance. The lines do show that, unlike

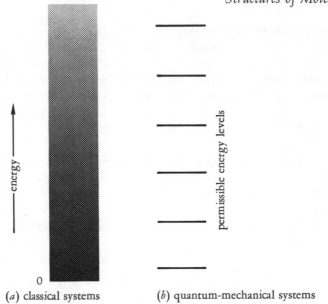

(*a*) classical systems   (*b*) quantum-mechanical systems

Figure 1–8   Energy diagrams to show that, for molecular systems, only certain energies are allowed.

the classical situation of Fig. 1–8*a* that applies to the energies of ordinary-sized objects, only certain energies are allowed to the molecular system.   As we proceed, we shall encounter such allowed-energy diagrams drawn for particular molecular motions.

The energies that are allowed by the quantum restrictions that apply to a given molecular motion depend on the properties of the molecule, i.e., its size, shape, and flexibility, as well as on the type of motion.   It follows that a study of the allowed energies might lead to information on these molecular details.   When radiation is absorbed or emitted by the molecule, the molecule must change its energy from one allowed amount to another.   We shall, in our study of molecules by means of spectroscopy, measure the energies of the quanta that are absorbed or emitted by a molecule; we shall use this information to deduce what the allowed energies of the molecule are; and, finally, we shall use the relations between these allowed energies and the molecular structure to determine this latter quantity.

One might, before proceeding, want to ask why the energies of molecular-scale particles are quantized. No answer can be given to this basic question. In more advanced courses the student will encounter a number of ways of deciding what the restrictions are, but these "ways" will be introduced arbitrarily. For example, an important equation that is often used in studies of molecular behavior, given by Erwin Schrödinger, permits us, often with some mathematical difficulty, to obtain relations between molecular properties and the energies that are allowed for any molecular motion. While it is satisfying to have such a method to apply to any molecular motion, it remains true that the Schrödinger equation is stated, not derived. It is accepted because it leads to agreement with experimental results. In a way, therefore, it does not explain the basis of quantum restrictions and we are still left with the need to accept these restrictions as a basic fact of nature.

A very useful qualitative generalization about these restrictions can, however, be made. This is that *the restrictions are increasingly important the smaller the region in which the particle is free to move. That is, of the whole range of energies fewer and more widely spaced ones are allowed the more restricted the motion of the particle.* On this basis we can expect that the quantum restrictions on translational energies of molecules are quite unimportant because each molecule is free to move in the ordinary-sized space of the container that confines the gas. Likewise, quantum restrictions are not observed in the world of balls, automobiles, airplanes, etc. On the other hand, the particles of a rotating molecule are confined to a volume about equal to that of the molecule. The atoms of a vibrating molecule are likewise confined to the small displacements that the flexibility of the bonds of the molecule allow. Finally, the electrons of a molecule are confined to the volume, or perhaps to a part of the volume, of the molecule. We thus expect that rotational, vibrational, and electronic motions will be subject to significant quantum restrictions or, as we often say, will be *quantized*. It is these restrictions that allow the properties of the molecule to be discovered by the methods of spectroscopy.

It might be mentioned that the most generally used method for relating molecular properties to the allowed energies depends on the Schrödinger equation. This equation is the molecular-dimension counterpart of Newton's laws of motion. In this introduction to spectroscopy it will be possible to obtain the necessary relations without use of Schrödinger's equation. As we proceed it will be apparent that there are close relations between ordinary, or *classical*, behavior and molecular, or *quantized*, behavior. We shall therefore be able to study molecules by the more familiar and easily handled equations of motion that we use for ordinary particles. The quantum restrictions can then be attached to these results. This procedure is one often used in spectroscopic studies.

1-5 BOLTZMANN DISTRIBUTION

One more general feature must be introduced before molecular energies, and the changes in these energies brought about by the absorption or emission of quanta of radiation, are related to the size, shape, and so forth, of molecules.

In the preceding section it was shown that the rotational, vibrational, and electronic energies of a molecule are quantized; i.e., only certain energies are allowed. In addition to knowing which energies are allowed, we shall want to be able to answer this question: If we have a gas sample with a large number of molecules, what fraction of the molecules will have energies corresponding to each of the allowed energies?

We can make use, to a certain extent, of the result that is obtained from a study of the classical, i.e., not quantized, translational motion. For this motion, the average kinetic energy is $\frac{1}{2}kT$ per degree of freedom. When quantized motions are considered, this result, although somewhat upset, is still a fair guide. We can decide, for example, that if a particular energy level is not much more than about kT above the lowest level, it should be appreciably populated, i.e., an appreciable fraction of the molecules of the sample will have this amount of energy. If, on the other hand, an energy level is considered that is of very much higher energy than kT, it can be expected that few molecules will have this high energy and the level will be little populated. The way in which molecules

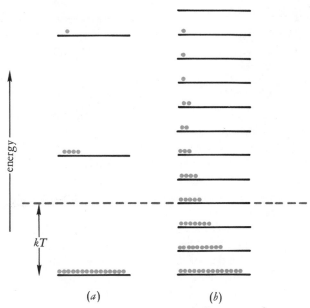

(a) (b)

Figure 1–9 The distribution of molecules throughout (a) widely spaced and (b) closely spaced allowed-energy levels.

distribute themselves throughout widely and closely spaced allowed energies is shown in Fig. 1–9.

The above ideas can be put in a more quantitative form. A relation which is basic to the understanding of molecular behavior relates the number of molecules n_i that occupy some energy level, say the ith level, to the number n_0 that occupy the lowest energy level. The relation, known as Boltzmann's distribution, is

$$\frac{n_i}{n_0} = e^{-(\epsilon_i - \epsilon_0)/kT}$$

where $\epsilon_i - \epsilon_0$ is the energy difference between the two levels, k is Boltzmann's constant already introduced, and T is the absolute temperature.

The importance of kT in determining the population of quantum states stems from its occurrence in this equation. One can readily verify that for $\epsilon_i - \epsilon_0$ not much greater than kT the ratio n_i/n_0 is not much less than unity. For $\epsilon_i - \epsilon_0$ much greater than kT, on the other hand, the ratio becomes very small. These features are illustrated by the two distributions shown in Fig. 1-9.

1-6   TYPES OF MOLECULAR SPECTROSCOPY

We shall see that radiation can be passed through a sample so that when the radiation quanta are absorbed by the molecules of the sample, the molecules increase their rotational or their vibrational or their electronic energy from one allowed value to one of the higher-energy allowed values. Furthermore, if the frequency, and thus quantum energy, range of the radiation is suitably chosen, one can, to some extent, affect a particular type of molecular energy.

Thus, if microwave radiation is used, the radiation quanta that are absorbed increase the rotational energy of the molecules and the relative positions of the allowed rotational energies of a molecule can be determined. Such studies constitute what can be called *rotational spectroscopy*.

In a similar manner, when infrared radiation is absorbed by a molecule, the vibrational energy of the molecule increases and the allowed vibrational energy level pattern can be investigated. Such studies constitute *vibrational spectroscopy*.

Finally, the absorption of visible and ultraviolet radiation can cause the electrons of a molecule to be excited from the arrangement that they ordinarily have in a molecule to some other allowed arrangement that has a higher energy. Measurements of visible and ultraviolet spectra and the deduction of the behavior of the electrons of a molecule from these spectra constitute *electronic spectroscopy*.

We now can proceed to analyze in more detail each of the three quantized types of molecular energy, how they are affected when radiation falls on a molecule, and how a study of the effect reveals much about the molecule itself.

SUMMARY

As a preliminary to the use of measurements of the absorption of radiation to deduce the properties of molecules, some general features of radiation and of molecular energies have been presented.

In addition, the techniques whereby the absorption of various wave-lengths, or frequencies, of radiation can be determined have been outlined.

Both the experimental methods and the molecular energies have been classified, and these classifications can, as the following chapters will reveal in some detail, be correlated as follows:

Molecular property studied	*Experimental region*
Rotation	Microwave
Vibration	Infrared
Electronic arrangement	Visible and ultraviolet

EXERCISES

1. The spectral region in which radiation has quantum energies higher than those of visible radiation is the ultraviolet region. Very often radiation in the ultraviolet region is described in terms of the wavelength of the radiation, expressed in angstrom units. A typical ultraviolet wavelength is 2000 A. Calculate ν and $\bar{\nu}$ for such radiation. Calculate $\Delta\epsilon$, the energy of a quantum of this radiation, and compare with the value given above for radiation in the visible region.

(Ans.: $\nu = 1.5 \times 10^{15}$ cycles/sec, $\bar{\nu} = 5 \times 10^4$ cm^{-1},
$$\Delta\epsilon = 9.9 \times 10^{-12} \text{ erg})$$

2. One often talks of radiation in the infrared region in terms of its wave number $\bar{\nu}$. Typical infrared radiation has $\bar{\nu} = 1000$ cm^{-1}. Calculate ν, λ, and $\Delta\epsilon$ for this radiation and notice that infrared radiation has quantum energies that are somewhat lower than those in the visible region.

(Ans.: $\nu = 3 \times 10^{13}$ cycles/sec, $\lambda = 0.001$ cm, $\Delta\epsilon = 2.0 \times 10^{-13}$ erg)

3. Beyond the infrared region in the direction of lower quantum energies is the microwave region. In this region radiation is usually characterized by its frequency ν. The numbers that are dealt with are more convenient if one uses megacycles per second rather than cycles per second (1 megacycle = 10^6 cycles). A typical microwave frequency is 20,000 megacycles/sec. Calculate $\bar{\nu}$, λ, and $\Delta\epsilon$ for this radiation.

(Ans.: $\bar{\nu} = 0.67$ cm^{-1}, $\lambda = 1.5$ cm, $\Delta\epsilon = 1.3 \times 10^{-16}$ erg)

4. Make a table so that the values of λ, ν, $\bar{\nu}$, and $\Delta\epsilon$ for visible radiation and for ultraviolet, infrared, and microwave radiation as calculated in the preceding exercises can be compared.

5. How many translational, rotational, and vibrational degrees of freedom are there in the molecules HCl, CO_2 (linear), H_2S (bent), CH_4 (tetrahedral)? Check to see that in each case the total number of degrees of freedom is 3 times the number of atoms in the molecule. (*Ans.: For CO_2: 3 translational, 2 rotational, 4 vibrational. For H_2S:*
3 translational, 3 rotational, 3 vibrational)

6. Calculate the number of molecules in a higher energy level relative to the number in a lower level if the levels are separated by an energy of 0.4×10^{-14} erg and the temperature is 25°C. (Notice after you have obtained your answer that 0.4×10^{-14} erg is rather less than the value of kT at this temperature.)

$$(Ans.: n_{high}/n_{low} = 0.91)$$

7. Calculate the number of molecules in a higher energy level relative to the number in a lower level if the levels are separated by an energy of 40×10^{-14} erg and the temperature is 25°C. (Notice that now the energy separation of the levels is greater than kT at this temperature.) $(Ans.: n_{high}/n_{low} = 6.0 \times 10^{-5})$

II

Rotational Spectra and the Size and Shape of Molecules

Now we shall delve into rotational spectroscopy; i.e., we shall deduce molecular properties from observations of the radiation which, when absorbed by a molecule, has the effect of increasing the rotational energy of the molecule. In outline, this introduction to rotational spectroscopy will have the following form. After some mention of the experimental methods used to obtain rotational spectra, the equations that describe the rotation of ordinary-sized objects will be set up. (These will probably be familiar to the student from studies in beginning college physics.) Then the quantum restrictions will be imposed so that the rotational energies the molecule is allowed to have can be determined. Next we shall investigate how radiation can interact with the molecule to change its rotational energy and we shall see how this compares with the actual, experimental measurements. Finally, a comparison of the expressions obtained for the allowed energies with the observed spectrum will provide us with the molecular structure information that we seek.

2–1   OBSERVATIONAL METHODS FOR
THE ABSORPTION OF RADIATION
BY ROTATING MOLECULES

Later in the chapter we shall verify that it is the absorption of quanta of radiation of the microwave region that changes the energy with which a molecule rotates. Let us first look, therefore, into some of the special features in this, the longest-wavelength region with which we shall be concerned.

Instrumentation for work in the microwave region is rather different from that used in all the other spectral regions to be studied. The microwave region is, as it were, halfway between the optical regions of the infrared, visible, and ultraviolet and the long-wavelength region of radio waves, where very different methods are used. (The relationship between these regions can be appreciated from Fig. 1–4 or by recalling that radio frequencies are of the order of kilocycles per second, that is, 10^3 cycles/sec; microwave frequencies are about 10^{11} cycles/sec; and visible radiation has frequencies of the order of 10^{15} cycles/sec.)

The techniques used in the microwave region are, therefore, rather more like those used in producing, propagating, and detecting radio and television waves than they are like the optical methods outlined so far. A schematic diagram of a microwave spectrometer is given in Fig. 2–1. The source of microwaves is an electronic device known as a klystron, illustrated in Fig. 2–2. An applied voltage accelerates electrons in a cavity in this tube, and this can be made to cause the cavity to emit radiation in the microwave region. In microwave spectroscopy no specific dispersing element is needed. The klystron source produces, at a given applied voltage, a beam of monochromatic microwave radiation. Furthermore, the frequency of this radiation is dependent on the voltage that is applied to the tube. In practice the applied voltage is varied over a given range, and in this way the emitted radiation can be made to sweep through a region of the microwave range.

The radiation is not handled with mirrors and lenses, but rather is conducted along a rectangular tube called a waveguide. At the far end of the waveguide is the detector. This consists of a quartz crystal that can be so tuned that it vibrates in response to

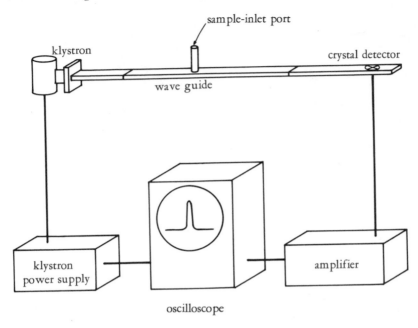

Figure 2–1 Simplified schematic diagram of a microwave spectrometer.

the vibrations of the microwave radiation. The vibrations of the quartz crystal produce an electrical signal which is amplified and displayed either as a recording on a chart or, more commonly, as a pattern on an oscilloscope screen. When the absorption of a sample is being studied, the vapor of the sample is put into the waveguide and its absorption leads to a diminished signal from the crystal detector at the wavelengths absorbed.

Now let us investigate, in more detail than in the preceding chapter, how objects rotate and, more particularly, the energies with which molecules rotate. It is such rotational energies that are changed when the absorptions that are detected in the microwave region occur.

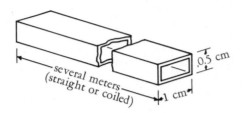

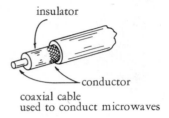

insulator

conductor

coaxial cable
used to conduct microwaves

a typical wave guide that,
in a microwave spectrometer,
serves as the sample cell

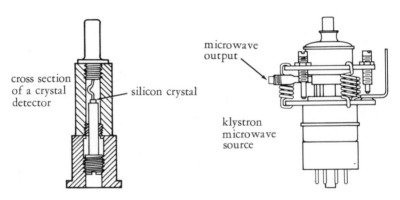

cross section
of a crystal
detector

silicon crystal

microwave
output

klystron
microwave
source

Figure 2–2   Some of the components used in a microwave
spectrometer.

2–2   ROTATION OF
ORDINARY-SIZED OBJECTS

The problem of how a diatomic molecule rotates can be approached by first considering the motion of an ordinary-sized ball
held by a string to a fixed point as shown in Fig. 2–3. Although
the kinetic energy for a particle so moving can be written down
immediately as $\frac{1}{2}mv^2$, where m is the mass of the particle and v is

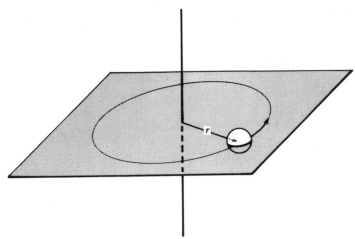

Figure 2–3   The rotation of a single particle about a fixed point.

its velocity, it is usually convenient to introduce other quantities to describe rotary motion. Thus, in rotational problems the frequency of rotation, i.e., the number of revolutions that the particle makes per second, is often used. Let us denote this by ν_{rot}. Another related quantity is the angular velocity defined as the number of angular units, or radians, swept out per second. Since there are 2π radians in a complete revolution, it follows that, if ω denotes the angular velocity in radians per second, the relation

$$\omega = 2\pi\nu_{rot} \tag{1}$$

can be written.

The rotational quantities ν_{rot} and ω can be related to the velocity v of the particle. If the particle is a distance r from the center of rotation, it will travel a distance $2\pi r$ in each revolution. In 1 sec it will travel $(2\pi r)\nu_{rot}$. This is, therefore, the velocity with which it travels, and we have the relations

$$v = 2\pi r\nu_{rot} \tag{2}$$

and

$$v = r\omega. \tag{3}$$

For rotating systems it is convenient to use expressions involving the angular velocity ω rather than the linear velocity v. The kinetic-energy expression $\frac{1}{2}mv^2$ can be converted to this rotational quantity and becomes

$$KE = \tfrac{1}{2}mr^2\omega^2. \tag{4}$$

Another quantity that is useful in treating rotational problems is suggested by this expression. The moment of inertia, denoted by I, is often used. It is defined for a system with many particles as $I = \Sigma m_i r_i^2$, where i numbers off the particles with mass m_i a distance r_i from the center of rotation of the system. For the simple system of Fig. 2–3, where the single particle of the system has mass m and is a distance r from the origin, we have

$$I = mr^2. \tag{5}$$

With this quantity we can rewrite Eq. (4) as

$$KE = \tfrac{1}{2}I\omega^2. \tag{6}$$

(We should recognize that this is the rotational counterpart of $KE = \frac{1}{2}mv^2$ with I taking the place of m and ω taking the place of v.)

Let us now describe the kinetic energy of rotation of a lopsided dumbbell which, clearly, will provide us with some background when we come to diatomic molecules. The kinetic energy can again be written in the form

$$KE = \tfrac{1}{2}m_1 v_1^2 + \tfrac{1}{2}m_2 v_2^2. \tag{7}$$

Now the rotation occurs about the center of gravity of the system which, according to Fig. 2–4, is located by r_1 and r_2. The velocities of the two particles are related to ω, which is a property of the rotating system, by equations like Eq. (3). We thus have

$$v_1 = r_1\omega \qquad \text{and} \qquad v_2 = r_2\omega. \tag{8}$$

Substitution in Eq. (7) gives

$$KE = \tfrac{1}{2}\omega^2(m_1 r_1^2 + m_2 r_2^2). \tag{9}$$

Substitution of the definition of I puts this in the neater form

$$KE = \tfrac{1}{2}I\omega^2. \tag{10}$$

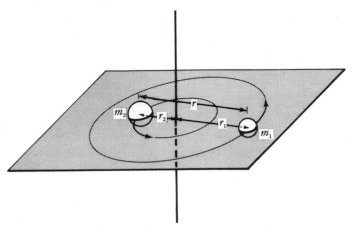

Figure 2–4   A rotating dumbbell.

The rotational energy of the dumbbell is, therefore, also given in terms of the angular velocity and the moment of inertia. It should also be clear that the expression of Eq. (10) will apply to the rotation of any system as long as the correct moment of inertia for the system is used.

Let us now work out what the moment of inertia is for the dumbbell system of Fig. 2–4. We have the moment of inertia in the form

$$I = m_1 r_1^2 + m_2 r_2^2. \tag{11}$$

This relation can be put in more convenient form by recalling that the center of gravity is located by r_1 and r_2 and, therefore, the relation

$$r_1 m_1 = r_2 m_2 \tag{12}$$

must hold. Separate expressions for r_1 and r_2 can be obtained by combining Eq. (12) with $r_1 + r_2 = r$ to give

$$r_1 = \frac{m_2}{m_1 + m_2} r \quad \text{and} \quad r_2 = \frac{m_1}{m_1 + m_2} r. \tag{13}$$

With these expressions we can eliminate r_1 and r_2 from Eq. (11) and obtain

$$I = \frac{m_1^2 m_2}{(m_1 + m_2)^2} r^2 + \frac{m_1 m_2^2}{(m_1 + m_2)^2} r^2$$

$$I = \frac{m_1 m_2}{m_1 + m_2} r^2. \tag{14}$$

The term involving the two masses occurs so frequently in the rotational and vibrational problems with which we shall be dealing that we give it the special name *reduced mass*. Furthermore, we introduce the symbol μ for this quantity and write

$$\mu = \frac{m_1 m_2}{m_1 + m_2}.$$

With this quantity the moment of inertia is neatly written as

$$I = \mu r^2. \tag{16}$$

(One should note the similarity in the form of this expression and the one used for I for the one-particle system treated earlier.)

The important results of this review of the classical rotation of a dumbbell are given by the expressions

$$KE = \tfrac{1}{2} I \omega^2, \tag{17}$$

where

$$I = \mu r^2 \tag{18}$$

and

$$\mu = \frac{m_1 m_2}{m_1 + m_2}. \tag{19}$$

Only one other point must be made in anticipation of what will be needed when molecular behavior is encountered. We shall see that angular momentum plays an important role. Here it is just mentioned that—by analogy with linear momentum, which is defined as the linear velocity times the mass—the angular momentum is defined as the angular velocity times the moment of inertia. Thus one can write

$$\text{angular momentum} = I\omega. \tag{20}$$

2-3   QUANTUM RESTRICTIONS—
ROTATION OF DIATOMIC MOLECULES

Now we consider a diatomic molecule, like HBr or CO, that is the equivalent of the dumbbell of the preceding section. The allowed rotational energies could be obtained for the molecular case by solution of Schrödinger's equation. Since solution of this equation requires considerable mathematical manipulation and a knowledge of more calculus than the reader may have at this stage, we resort to the often-used procedure of adding the quantum restrictions to the classical equations. In this way we can arrive at the correct result with little mathematical difficulty.

It turns out that the quantum restrictions that were discussed in the preceding chapter are often most easily expressed in terms of restrictions on the angular momentum rather than on the energy. One finds, furthermore, that the allowed amounts of angular momentum are generally multiples of the quantity $h/2\pi$, where h is Planck's constant. The angular momenta that are allowed for a diatomic molecule, for example, are given by the expression

angular momentum

$$= I\omega = \sqrt{J(J+1)}\,\frac{h}{2\pi} \quad J = 0, 1, 2, \ldots, \quad (21)$$

where J can have the integral values indicated. Thus the rotating molecule, according to this restriction, can have angular momenta of 0, $\sqrt{2}(h/2\pi)$, $\sqrt{6}(h/2\pi)$, $\sqrt{12}(h/2\pi)$, . . . , but cannot rotate with angular velocities that would give it any other angular momenta.

The above expression is typical of many that are encountered when the allowed molecular momenta, or energies, are studied. The allowed quantities are usually obtained when various integral values are inserted into a formula. In this case, for instance, the symbol J has been written in the equation and, as the addendum $J = 0, 1, 2, \ldots$ indicates, the formula gives the various allowed values of the angular momentum when the various integers are inserted for J. Thus the restriction, or quantization, of the angular momentum can be expressed by a formula that involves integers; and these integers are known as *quantum numbers*.

We are more interested in the allowed rotational energies, and we can now calculate them. The classical result for the rotational energy obtained in the preceding section, that is,

$$KE = \tfrac{1}{2}I\omega^2, \tag{22}$$

can be written as

$$KE = \frac{1}{2}\frac{(I\omega)^2}{I}. \tag{23}$$

Now the restriction on $I\omega$ given by Eq. (21) can be inserted to convert this classical equation to the quantum-mechanical one appropriate to the rotation of a molecule. We obtain

$$\epsilon_{rot} = \frac{h^2}{8\pi^2 I}J(J + 1) \quad \left(I = 0, 1, 2, \ldots, \right. \tag{24}$$

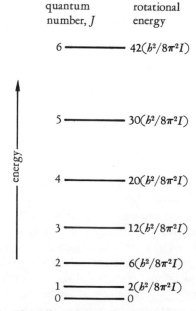

quantum number, J	rotational energy
6	$42(h^2/8\pi^2 I)$
5	$30(h^2/8\pi^2 I)$
4	$20(h^2/8\pi^2 I)$
3	$12(h^2/8\pi^2 I)$
2	$6(h^2/8\pi^2 I)$
1	$2(h^2/8\pi^2 I)$
0	0

Figure 2-5 The allowed rotational energies of a diatomic molecule as expressed by Eq. (24).

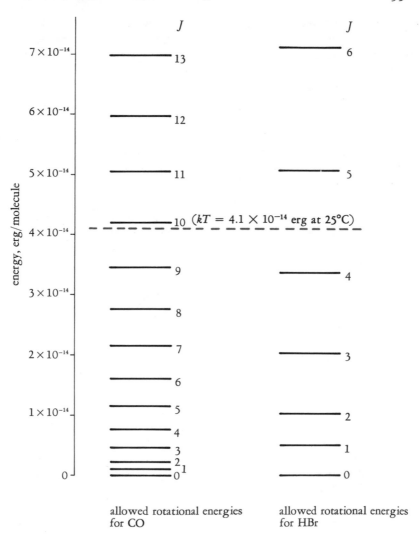

Figure 2–6 Some of the allowed rotational energies for CO ($\mu = 11.4 \times 10^{-24}$ g, $r = 1.13$ A, $I = 14.5 \times 10^{-40}$ g-cm²) and HBr ($\mu = 1.64 \times 10^{-24}$ g, $r = 1.41$ A, $I = 3.3 \times 10^{-40}$ g-cm²). These energies are compared with the value of kT at 25°C.

where ϵ_{rot} is written for the energies with which the molecule is allowed to rotate. Equation (24) is the most important expression for rotational spectroscopy studies. It shows how the allowed rotational energies depend on the molecular property I and on an integer denoted by J.

The allowed rotational energies, as given by Eq. (24), for a diatomic molecule form the pattern shown by the horizontal lines of Fig. 2–5.

If values of I, obtained by methods to be explained shortly, for HBr and CO are now used, the allowed rotational energy level diagrams for these two specific examples can be drawn to scale and compared. This is done in Fig. 2–6. One sees here the effect, also apparent from inspection of the form of Eq. (24), of the moment of inertia I on the spacing of the energy levels. Thus, since I_{CO} is greater than I_{HBr} and since the moment of inertia appears in the denominator of Eq. (24), the spacing between the allowed energies becomes less as the moment of inertia becomes greater.

It is interesting to compare the energy scale of Fig. 2–6 with our previous discussion about the significance of the energy amount kT. At room temperature kT has the value 4.1×10^{-14} erg. Comparison with Fig. 2–6 shows that for these examples there are many rotational energy levels that have energies that are less than or in the range of kT. It follows from the discussion of the Boltzmann distribution in Sec. 1–5 that many of these rotational levels will be appreciably occupied at room temperature, i.e., many of the molecules of a gas will have energies corresponding to $J = 0$, $J = 1$, $J = 2$, ...

We have now deduced enough about the rotation of a diatomic molecule that we are in a position to understand, and use, the measurements that constitute a rotational spectrum.

2–4   ROTATIONAL SPECTRA AND
BOND LENGTHS OF DIATOMIC MOLECULES

Let us first calculate, as we promised in Sec. 2–1, what radiation has quanta of such energy that, when a molecule absorbs one quantum, it will change its rotational energy from one allowed value to the next higher allowed value. According to Fig. 2–6 the spacing between allowed rotational energies for small molecules is about 10^{-15} erg. According to Planck's relation, $\Delta\epsilon = h\nu$, radiation will have quanta of this energy if the radiation has a frequency $\nu = \Delta\epsilon/h$ of about 10^{11} cycles/sec. Furthermore, this frequency implies a wavelength $\lambda = c/\nu$ of about 1 cm. When this value is compared with the radiation ranges given in Fig. 1–4, it is seen that microwave radiation has quanta which are of the energy corresponding to the separation of rotational energy levels.

With this guide one might be led to perform an experiment in which a beam of microwave radiation is passed through a gaseous sample of diatomic molecules. Such experiments have, in fact, been performed, and it is found that a number of absorptions at different wavelengths, or frequencies, occur. In Table 2–1 the wavelengths, frequencies, and quantum energies that would be absorbed by CO in such an experiment are listed. These results are also shown as a rather schematic absorption spectrum in Fig. 2–7.

(It must now be admitted that it is rather difficult to find experimental data for diatomic molecules to illustrate the discussion. It is true that radiation quanta in the microwave region are of the right size to cause many molecules to increase their rotational energy from one allowed value to another. However, diatomic molecules have relatively small moments of inertia and therefore widely

Table 2–1

The Absorption of Radiation by CO That Can Be Attributed to Changes in the Rotational Energy of the Molecule

Wavelength of observed absorption line, cm	Frequency of absorption line, cycles/sec	Energies of quanta absorbed, ergs	Rotational transition assigned to observed absorption line
0.260	1.15×10^{11}	7.61×10^{-16}	$J = 0 \rightarrow J = 1$
0.130	2.30×10^{11}	15.22×10^{-16}	$J = 1 \rightarrow J = 2$
0.0877	3.46×10^{11}	22.8×10^{-16}	$J = 2 \rightarrow J = 3$
0.0650	4.61×10^{11}	30.4×10^{-16}	$J = 3 \rightarrow J = 4$

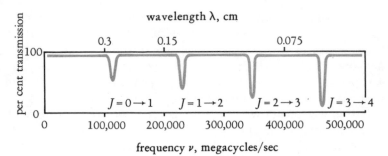

Figure 2-7 **Microwave absorption of CO (schematic). The absorption lines occur at the frequencies at which radiation quanta can change the energy of the CO molecules from one allowed rotational energy to the next higher allowed energy. The energy levels involved are indicated in terms of the values of the quantum number *J*.**

spaced allowed rotational energies. They generally require radiation quanta between the microwave and the infrared region, and no convenient instruments have been available for work in this spectroscopic "no-man's-land." The data of Table 2-1 have been extended by comparison with the spectra of linear molecules that show the same spectral pattern as do diatomic molecules.)

Now, can we understand the absorptions of radiation given in Table 2-1 or Fig. 2-7 on the basis of the molecular energy level pattern of the type shown in Fig. 2-3? We can if we attribute each absorption to one of the rotational energy jumps indicated by the arrows in Fig. 2-8. Thus, the first absorption line, at $\lambda = 0.260$ cm, is attributed to quanta being absorbed and increasing the rotational energy of the CO molecule from that corresponding to $J = 0$ to that corresponding to $J = 1$. In view of Eq. (24), these quanta must have energies equal to $\epsilon_{J=1} - \epsilon_{J=0}$, or

$$\frac{h^2}{8\pi^2 I}(1)(2) - \frac{h^2}{8\pi^2 I}(0) = \frac{h^2}{8\pi^2 I}(2).$$

Now, by equating the energy of the quanta that are absorbed, and thereby produce this first absorption line, with $(h^2/8\pi^2 I)(2)$, we

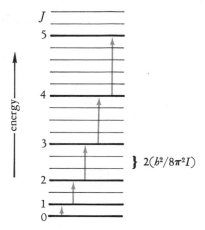

Figure 2–8 The rotational energy transitions that lead to the absorption lines in the microwave region. Note that each arrow is longer than the preceding one by an amount equivalent to $2(h^2/8\pi^2I)$.

can, as we shall see, obtain a value for the moment of inertia of the molecules of the sample.

The second absorption line in the spectrum of Fig. 2–7 occurs at a wavelength half that of the first or, more to the point here, at twice the frequency or quantum energy. It is possible to identify this second absorption line with quanta being absorbed by CO molecules that are initially rotating with an energy corresponding to $J = 1$ and raising their energy to that corresponding to $J = 2$. The quanta that would do this would have an energy of $\epsilon_{J=2} - \epsilon_{J=1}$, or

$$\frac{h^2}{8\pi^2I}(2)(3) - \frac{h^2}{8\pi^2I}(1)(2) = \frac{h^2}{8\pi^2I}(4).$$

Again the quantum energies at the absorption line can be equated, this time to $(h^2/8\pi^2I)(4)$, to obtain a value of I.

In a similar way each absorption line in the spectrum can be identified with a transition from one rotational energy level to the next higher one. These transitions are indicated by the vertical arrows in Fig. 2–8. That the observed absorption lines are correctly assigned to particular transitions is verified by the fact that essentially the same value of I is obtained from each one of the calculations, of the type illustrated above, that can be made.

Perhaps an even easier way to compare the observed spectrum with the arrows of Fig. 2–8 is to notice that each arrow is longer, i.e., the energy change that it represents is greater, than the preceding arrow by an amount $(h^2/8\pi^2 I)(2)$. The difference in quantum energies between adjacent absorption lines in the spectrum can therefore be identified with the quantity $(h^2/8\pi^2 I)(2)$. In this way we also can evaluate $(h^2/8\pi^2 I)(2)$ from the spacing between the lines of the observed rotational spectrum. With either procedure, we deduce, by comparing our theory of molecular rotation with the observed spectrum of the CO molecule,

$$(2)\frac{h^2}{8\pi^2 I_{\mathrm{CO}}} = 7.61 \times 10^{-16} \text{ erg.}$$

From this we obtain, after insertion of numerical values and rearrangement,

$$I_{\mathrm{CO}} = 1.45 \times 10^{-39} \text{ g-cm}^2.$$

Although the moment of inertia is a molecular property, it is generally more convenient to deal with the internuclear distance. The relation $I_{\mathrm{CO}} = \mu_{\mathrm{CO}} r_{\mathrm{CO}}^2$ can be used after the calculation

$$\mu_{\mathrm{CO}} = \frac{m_{\mathrm{C}} m_{\mathrm{O}}}{m_{\mathrm{C}} + m_{\mathrm{O}}} = \frac{(12)(16)/(6.023 \times 10^{23})^2}{28/(6.023 \times 10^{23})} = 1.14 \times 10^{-23} \text{ g.}$$

Finally, we obtain, in this example, our desired result

$$r_{\mathrm{CO}} = \sqrt{\frac{I_{\mathrm{CO}}}{\mu_{\mathrm{CO}}}} = \sqrt{\frac{1.45 \times 10^{-39}}{1.14 \times 10^{-23}}} = 1.13 \times 10^{-8} \text{ cm} = 1.13 \text{ A.}$$

In this illustrative calculation, values have been rounded off to three significant figures. The power of microwave spectral studies is perhaps more emphatically shown if full use is made of the precision of the measured absorption frequencies. The frequency of the radiation that causes the $J = 0$ to $J = 1$ transition in CO is actually reported by O. R. Gilliam, C. M. Johnson, and W. Gordy in Vol. 78, page 140, of *Physical Review* to be 115.2706×10^9 cycles/sec. As previously indicated, the energy of quanta of this frequency is equal to $(2)(h^2/8\pi^2 I_{CO})$. Calculations of I_{CO} and then of r_{CO} lead, if all significant figures are retained, to the remarkable result

$$r_{CO} = 1.128227 \text{ A}.$$

The retention of all these significant figures implies that the bond length is known to within 10^{-14} cm or approximately one-tenth of the nuclear diameter. A number of complications, principally the fact that, as we shall see, the molecule is continually vibrating and the bond length is some effective or average value, enter to make the result less significant than implied. It is, however, well to be impressed by the potential precision with which the dimensions of molecules can be measured by means of microwave spectroscopy.

This simple example has illustrated a procedure that can be used to measure the internuclear distance, or bond length, of diatomic molecules. Some further results are summarized in Table 2–2. We have come, therefore, to the first of the molecular structure results that can be obtained from spectroscopic studies. One should allow oneself to be impressed by the way in which one is led very directly into the world of molecular dimensions by a comparison of the

Table 2–2
Results on the Size of Diatomic Molecules Obtained from Studies of Rotational Energy Level Spacings

Molecule	Moment of inertia, $g\text{-}cm^2$	Reduced mass, g	Bond length, A
CO	14.5×10^{-40}	11.4×10^{-24}	1.128
NO	16.5×10^{-40}	12.4×10^{-24}	1.151
HF	1.34×10^{-40}	1.59×10^{-24}	0.917
HCl	2.65×10^{-40}	1.63×10^{-24}	1.275
HBr	3.31×10^{-40}	1.65×10^{-24}	1.414
HI	4.29×10^{-40}	1.66×10^{-24}	1.604
NaCl	129×10^{-40}	23.2×10^{-24}	2.361
CsCl	393×10^{-40}	46.5×10^{-24}	2.904

frequencies of the radiation that are absorbed with the allowed rotational energy expression of Eq. (24).

2–5   INTERACTION OF RADIATION
WITH ROTATING MOLECULES

Conspicuously absent from Table 2–2 are homonuclear diatomic molecules H_2, N_2, and so forth.   Such molecules do not, in fact, absorb radiation in the microwave region, and an explanation of the absence of a rotational spectrum for such molecules allows a few comments on the way in which the beam of microwave radiation interacts with the rotating molecule to be made.   (It can be mentioned that it is this failure of N_2, O_2, and CO_2 to absorb significant amounts of microwave radiation that allows radar, which operates with microwave frequencies, to be used as a detecting device without serious loss of signal due to absorption by the atmosphere through which the signals must pass.)

To understand how the rotating molecule can grab energy from the radiation beam and thereby increase its rotational energy, one must make use of the wave-nature picture of the radiation.   It will be recalled that, in this view, the molecule sees the radiation as an oscillating electric field.   For our present purpose it is enough to know that an electric field is defined as an electrical effect that tends to move charged particles one way or the other.

Let us now suppose that the rotating diatomic molecule has a dipole, i.e., one end is more positively charged and the other end is more negatively charged.   (All molecules like HCl, CO, and NO will have positive and negative ends.   Homonuclear diatomic molecules like H_2 and N_2 have necessarily identical ends and therefore no dipole moment.)   Can such a rotating polar molecule interact with the electric field of the microwave radiation?

If, when the molecule is in the position indicated in Fig. 2–9*a*, the electric field is such that it pushes plus charges up and therefore minus charges down, it will tend to make the molecule rotate faster. Now if, when the molecule has rotated to the position of Fig. 2–9*b* the radiation has also moved along to its next cycle, as indicated, the interacting force will still operate to make the molecule rotate faster.   Thus, if the frequency of the radiation and that of the

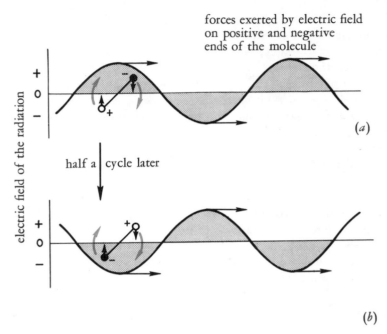

forces exerted by electric field
on positive and negative
ends of the molecule

electric field of the radiation

half a cycle later

(a)

(b)

Figure 2–9   The interaction of the electric field of the radiation falling on a molecule with the dipole of the molecule.
For the frequency of the radiation the same as the rotational
frequency of the molecule, the effect of the interaction forces
can be to make the molecule rotate faster.

molecular rotation are equal, the electric field can interact with the
molecular dipole and can keep pushing the molecule to a higher
rotational energy. If frequencies of radiation different from the one
that coincided with the rotational frequency were to fall on the
molecule, the pushes would not all be in the same direction and the
rotational energy of the molecule would not tend to change. This
wave-nature picture supplements our previous quantum picture and
adds the important new feature that only molecules with dipole
moments can interact with radiation to give a rotational spectrum.
The absence of absorption of microwave radiation by molecules such
as H_2, N_2, and O_2 is thus explained. The explanation, however,

leaves us with the fact that the bond length of such molecules cannot be measured in the way illustrated for CO. Other spectroscopic methods are available, as will be seen later.

A further restriction, besides that requiring the molecule to have a dipole, exists on the rotational energy changes that can occur. One finds, by a derivation that must make use of solutions to the Schrödinger equation, that when a molecule interacts with radiation, it can only change its rotational energy to the next higher or next lower allowed energy. One usually expresses this as a *selection rule* and writes

$$\Delta J = \pm 1.$$

When absorption of radiation is studied, only the change $\Delta J = +1$ is appropriate. All the arrows of Fig. 2–8 have been drawn to conform to this selection rule. The agreement of the observed spectral pattern, as in Fig. 2–7, with that expected on the basis of the arrows of Fig. 2–8 provides experimental verification of the restriction that allows the molecule to move up only one rotational energy step at a time.

2–6   EXTENSION OF THE METHOD
TO OTHER MOLECULES

Most spectroscopic methods become progressively more difficult to apply as larger molecules are studied. The spectroscopy of rotating molecules is no exception. Nevertheless, many molecules have been studied and many valuable, precise molecular structure data have been obtained. Here some of the difficulties that occur in the study of molecules other than diatomic molecules will be mentioned and some of the results for generally shaped molecules will be indicated.

Let us first take the smallest possible step beyond diatomic molecules and consider linear triatomic molecules. A general difficulty in analyzing the data for polyatomic molecules will be illustrated.

To be specific, we shall consider the linear molecule OCS, carbonyl sulfide, which has been much studied by microwave spectroscopy. (The student will be more familiar with the related molecules: carbon dioxide, CO_2, and carbon disulfide, CS_2. These, however, are symmetric linear molecules, i.e., they can be represented by O=C=O and S=C=S, and necessarily have zero dipole moments. They cannot, therefore, be studied by means of microwave spectroscopy.) Since such molecules are the counterparts of a thin rod, as are diatomic molecules, the same rotational energy expression as before applies, that is,

$$\epsilon_{rot} = \frac{h^2}{8\pi^2 I} J(J+1) \qquad J = 0, 1, 2, \ldots$$

In accordance with this similarity to diatomic molecules the same spectral pattern of equispaced absorptions in the microwave region, as shown by the data of Table 2–3, is observed. In a manner exactly analogous to the procedure for diatomic molecules, i.e., the comparison of the observed absorptions with the transitions between allowed rotational energies, the quantity $h^2/8\pi^2 I$ and thus the moment of inertia I for any linear molecule can be found. The data for OCS given in Table 2–3 yield the result

$$I_{O^{16}C^{12}S^{32}} = 138.0 \times 10^{-40} \text{ g-cm}^2,$$

Table 2–3

The Frequencies at Which Radiation Is Absorbed by $O^{16}C^{12}S^{32}$ in the Microwave Region and the Assignment of These Absorptions to Rotational Transitions

Transition	Frequency of radiation absorbed,[a] cycles/sec	Calculated value of $h^2/8\pi^2 I$, cycles/sec	Calculated value of I, g-cm²
$J = 1 \rightarrow J = 2$	24.3259×10^9	6.08149×10^9	137.9450×10^{-40}
$J = 2 \rightarrow J = 3$	36.4882×10^9	6.08147×10^9	137.9454×10^{-40}
$J = 3 \rightarrow J = 4$	48.65164×10^9	6.08145×10^9	137.9459×10^{-40}
$J = 4 \rightarrow J = 5$	60.81408×10^9	6.08141×10^9	137.9468×10^{-40}

[a] Absorption at about 12×10^9 cycles/sec would be expected to correspond to a change in molecular rotation from J = 0 to J = 1. This frequency was, however, beyond the range of the instrument.

Structures of Molecules

where the isotopic species present in the molecules studied have been specifically indicated for reasons that will now be made clear.

Now, even with the assumption that the molecule is linear, how can one deduce the two bond lengths r_{CO} and r_{CS} from the one measured quantity? Obviously, we need another measured quantity if we are to evaluate these two unknowns. A procedure often resorted to, in view of this common problem of more structural unknowns than measured moments of inertia, is that of studying a different isotopic species, such as $O^{16}C^{12}S^{34}$ in our example. (To a satisfactory approximation one can assume that the bond length is not changed if the mass of a nucleus is changed, that is, $r_{C^{12}S^{32}} = r_{C^{12}S^{34}}$.) If one measures the rotational spectrum of $O^{16}C^{12}S^{34}$, one finds

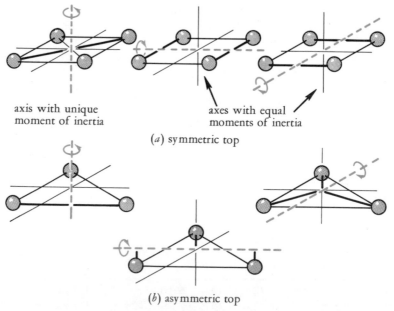

axis with unique
moment of inertia

axes with equal
moments of inertia

(*a*) symmetric top

(*b*) asymmetric top

Figure 2–10   Examples of (*a*) symmetric- and (*b*) asymmetric-top molecules. The axes for the principal moments of inertia are shown. The heavy lines show the distances that enter into the calculation of $I = \Sigma m_i r_i^2$ about these axes. For symmetric tops, two of the three moments of inertia are equal. For asymmetric tops, all moments of inertia are different.

$$I_{O^{16}C^{12}S^{34}} = 141.4 \times 10^{-40} \text{ g-cm}^2.$$

Now one can use the values of the two moments of inertia, $I_{O^{16}C^{12}S^{32}}$ and $I_{O^{16}C^{12}S^{34}}$, and can deduce the values of the two unknowns r_{CO} and r_{CS}. The calculation depends on locating the center of gravity and expressing the moment of inertia for each molecule in terms of the unknowns r_{CO} and r_{CS}. The measured moment of inertia and the expression for the moment of inertia in terms of r_{CO} and r_{CS} provide for each molecule, an equation in these two unknowns. The two equations that are set up can then be solved for the two unknowns and the results

$$r_{CO} = 1.165 \text{ A} \qquad r_{CS} = 1.558 \text{ A}$$

are obtained.

The analysis of a linear molecule—and this also applies to diatomic molecules—leads, if only one isotopic species is studied, to only one moment-of-inertia value. More generally shaped poly-atomic molecules will have two or three different principal moments of inertia, and analysis of the rotational spectra of such molecules can sometimes lead to values for these moments of inertia. In rotational spectral studies it is convenient to classify molecules as *symmetric tops* if they have two of their three principal moments of inertia equal and *asymmetric tops* if all three principal moments of inertia are different. The two categories are illustrated in Fig. 2–10. In the first category are molecules such as

(umbrella shaped)   **(planar, symmetric ring)**   **(double umbrella)**

whereas in the second category are molecules like

$$
\begin{array}{c}
\text{Cl} \\
| \\
\text{H} \quad \text{C} \quad \text{H} \\
\diagdown \quad \diagup \\
\text{C} \\
\| \\
\end{array}
$$

The energy level patterns for the rotation of such molecules are similar to, but more complicated than, those of a linear molecule. It follows that when transition arrows are drawn to represent the various quanta that might be absorbed, these more complicated diagrams will not lead to a simple pattern of arrows each of which is longer than the preceding one by a constant amount. It follows also that the rotational spectrum of an asymmetric-top molecule will show, not a nicely arranged series of absorptions but, rather, a complicated pattern.

Figure 2–11 illustrates the type of absorption pattern found for asymmetric-top molecules in the microwave region. In spite of the added complexity, one can proceed, as in the diatomic case, to match up the absorptions with transitions between allowed energies. When this can be done, the three principal moments of inertia of the molecule can be deduced. Again one can study different isotopic

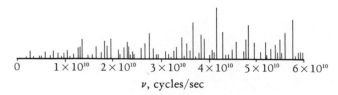

ν, cycles/sec

Figure 2–11 The complexity of the pattern of rotational absorption lines found in the microwave spectrum of an asymmetric-top molecule.

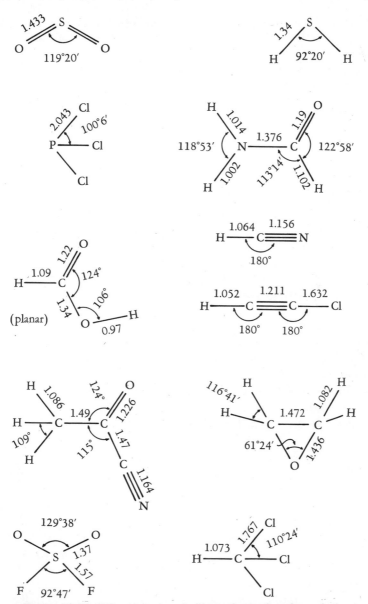

Figure 2-12 The shape and dimensions of a few of the molecules whose rotational spectra have been studied.

species in order to obtain additional moment-of-inertia data. These sometimes allow all the bond lengths and bond angles of the molecule to be determined. Some results are given in Fig. 2–12. As this figure suggests, the methods described here have led to a wealth of very precise and reliable results for the dimensions of small molecules.

2–7   EXTENSIONS AND SUBTLETIES

It must be admitted that even for diatomic molecules everything in rotational spectroscopy is not as pat and simple as much of the earlier discussion suggests. It is worthwhile pointing out, even in an introduction such as this, two of the finer details that enter.

First of all, as might have been anticipated on the basis of the analogy between molecules and ball-and-spring assemblies, as the molecule rotates faster and faster, centrifugal distortion sets in and the springs, or bonds, are very slightly stretched. When this happens, the moment of inertia I increases a little. The very careful measurements of absorption frequencies that can be made in the microwave region allows, as the data of Table 2–3 show, even this very minor feature of molecular behavior to be revealed. In very precise work one takes account of this effect and reports moment-of inertia data for the $J = 0$ rotational state in which there is no centrifugal distortion.

One other detail that more advanced treatments of rotational spectroscopy would deal with will be mentioned. So far we have pretty much ignored the role of the nuclei of the molecule—except in so far as they contribute mass and determine the moment of inertia. It turns out that, like the whole molecule, individual nuclei also may rotate about an axis through their center of gravity. The molecule is therefore a rather complicated system of rotating parts in a rotating whole. The energy of interaction between the rotating nuclei and the molecule is, however, very small. The result of this is that the energy levels for molecular rotation that have been discussed in this chapter are only slightly disturbed by the rotations of the nuclei that are occurring at the same time. In fact, one observes that for molecules containing rotating nuclei some absorptions are "split" into several closely spaced absorptions as illustrated

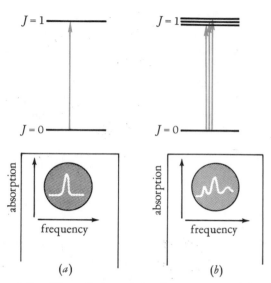

Figure 2–13 The splitting of the $J = 1$ rotational level that can occur if the molecule contains a nucleus with angular momentum. Below the energy-level diagrams are the oscilloscope patterns that would be obtained for the absorption lines. [The pattern in (*b*) is actually obtained for the molecule DCN in which the nucleus of the nitrogen atom has one unit of angular momentum and causes the splitting. Observed by Simmons, Anderson, and Gordy, *Phys. Rev.*, **77**, 77(1950).]

in Fig. 2–13. This splitting can be attributed to the changes brought about in the molecular rotation by the rotating nuclei. This subject will not be treated further, and it will only be stated that if the fine structure of the absorption lines is studied, one learns something of the way in which nuclei rotate as well as the way in which molecules rotate.

SUMMARY

When radiation of the microwave region passes through a gas sample, the molecules of the gas may absorb certain wavelengths of the radiation, i.e., may absorb quanta of certain energies. This

absorbed radiant energy increases the rotational energy of the absorbing molecule from one rotational state to the next higher energy
state. Measured values of the wavelength or frequency, and thus
the quantum energy, of the radiation that is absorbed are compared
with the expressions that relate the allowed rotational energies to
the moments of inertia of the molecule. In this way the moments
of inertia and, to some extent, the lengths of the bonds and the
angles between the bonds in the molecule can be deduced. In favor-
able cases where not too many bond angles and bond lengths are
needed to describe the shape and dimensions of the molecule, the
measurements of these molecular dimensions can be made with great
precision.

In spite of our general understanding of the way in which
changes in molecular energies lead to absorption of microwave
radiation, it is often a problem of considerable difficulty, and a time-
consuming task, to match up the individual absorption lines that
are observed in the microwave spectrum with particular transitions
between allowed rotational energy levels of the molecule. This is
particularly true for asymmetric-top molecules, and it is such molecules that constitute the largest class that interests the chemist.
Many valuable molecular structure data remain, for the time being,
hidden within the complexities of these spectra. The discovery of
a systematic way for analyzing microwave spectral data of such
molecules has yet to be developed, and the discovery of such a
technique will make available to the chemist a fund of precise molecular structure information. Such information will be of invaluable aid in our continuous attempts to understand the nature of the
chemical bond better.

Another area, from which similarly valuable molecular structure information will come, is that of the microwave spectroscopy
of gases at high temperatures. In the past, most microwave spectroscopy has been done at room temperature, and, it is certainly
true, most of the small gaseous molecules that exist at room temperature have been rather completely studied. At a thousand degrees or
so, however, many materials vaporize or decompose to give small
molecules that could, if the experimental difficulties involved were
overcome, be studied by microwave spectroscopy. A whole new
and exciting group of small molecules whose structure and bonding

are as yet little understood could then be approached with the powerful tool of microwave spectroscopy.

EXERCISES

1. Calculate the moment of inertia of a dumbbell system like that of Fig. 2–4 if one particle has a mass of 1 g, the other a mass of 2 g, and the distance between the particles is 10 cm.

(*Ans.: I = 67 g-cm²*)

2. Calculate the moment of inertia of the molecule NO, which has an equilibrium bond length of 1.151 A = 1.151 × 10⁻⁸ cm.

(*Ans.: I = 16.5 × 10⁻⁴⁰ g-cm²*)

3. To appreciate how much less space the atoms of a molecule have to move in as compared to the particles of an ordinary-sized system, calculate the circumference of the path of the 1-g mass of Exercise 1 and that of the nitrogen atom of the NO molecule dealt with in Exercise 2. (Recall now the discussion of Sec. 1–3 regarding quantum restrictions.)

(*Ans.: For 1-g mass 2πr = 42 cm. For N atom 2πr = 3.9 × 10⁻⁸ cm*)

4. The moment of inertia of the molecule HCl is 2.64 × 10⁻⁴⁰ g-cm². Calculate some of the energies ϵ_{rot} and the angular velocities ω with which the molecule is allowed to rotate.

(*Ans.: J = 1, ϵ_{rot} = 0.42 × 10⁻¹⁴ erg, ω = 5.6 × 10¹² radians/sec*
J = 2, ϵ_{rot} = 1.26 × 10⁻¹⁴ erg, ω = 9.8 × 10¹² radians/sec)

5. The internuclear distance for the diatomic molecule NO is 1.151 A. What will be the energies of the first four rotational energy levels? (*Ans.: J = 1, ϵ_{rot} = 6.7 × 10⁻¹⁶ erg*)

6. Using Fig. 2–6 and reading off the energies of the levels as well as the figure allows, tabulate the energies of the quanta that would have to be absorbed to allow the HBr molecule to increase its rotational energy from the energy levels labeled J = 0 to J = 1, J = 1 to J = 2, J = 2 to J = 3, and so forth. Alongside the tabulated quantum energies add the frequencies, in cycles per second and megacycles per second, to which these quanta correspond. Finally, make a schematic absorption spectrum for the microwave spectral region, like that of Fig. 2–7, for the HBr molecules.

7. One observes that HCl gas absorbs radiation that has wave numbers of about 20.7, 41.5, 62.3, 83.0, 103.8 cm⁻¹. . . . (a) Assign

each of these absorptions to a particular rotational transition. (b) Convert these values of $\bar{\nu}$ to quantum energies $\Delta\epsilon$ and deduce, from the values of $\Delta\epsilon$ for several of the absorptions, values for the moment of inertia of the HCl molecule. (c) Using the fact that the spacing between adjacent absorptions can be identified with $2(h^2/8\pi^2 I)$, obtain a value of the moment of inertia. (d) Calculate the reduced mass of HCl assuming that we are dealing with the chlorine isotope Cl^{35}. (e) Using the values of parts (d) and either (b) or (c) obtain a value for the bond length of the HCl molecule. (*Ans.*: (*b*) *for* $\bar{\nu} = 20.7\ cm^{-1}$, $\nu = 6.2 \times 10^{11}\ cycles/sec$,

$$\Delta\epsilon = 4.1 \times 10^{-15} erg,\ I = 2.7 \times 10^{-40}\ g\text{-}cm^2)$$

8. Using the allowed rotational energies given by Eq. (24) or Fig. 2–5, perform the calculations that give the column of values for $h^2/8\pi^2 I$ for OCS in Table 2–3 from the reported frequencies and the assigned transitions.

9. To slide-rule accuracy, verify that the frequency of the $J = 2$ to $J = 3$ transition given in Table 2–3 leads to the value given for I_{OCS}.

10. Give two additional examples of linear molecules, symmetric-top molecules, and asymmetric-top molecules.

An additional type of molecule, not mentioned so far, is that in which the three principal moments of inertia are equal. Since this is the situation in a sphere, these molecules are said to be spherical tops. Give two examples of spherical-top molecules.

III

Vibrational Spectra and the
Flexibility of Molecules

Let us now move up to radiation in the next higher range of quantum energies, i.e., infrared radiation, and see what we can learn about molecules by studying the absorption of this radiation. It has already been mentioned that the molecular motion that is altered by the absorption of quanta of infrared radiation is vibrational motion. Studies of the vibrational spectra of molecules lead to information on the flexibility of molecules, i.e., the ease with which the bond lengths and bond angles can be distorted from the values that they have in the equilibrium configuration of the molecule.

If our study continues to be based on molecules in the gas phase, an added complexity occurs. While the vibrational energy of a gas-phase molecule changes as a result, for example, of the absorption of a quantum of radiation, so also may the rotational energy of the molecule change. This combination of vibrational and rotational effects can be avoided by considering molecules that are in a pure liquid or in a solution. The close neighbors of such molecules are effective in preventing molecular rotations such as occur for a free gas-phase molecule. The vibrations of the molecule are, however, little affected by these neighbors. Let us therefore first investigate the way in which such a nonrotating molecule can vibrate and how changes in the molecular vibrational energy can be studied spectroscopically. In the following chapter we shall consider molecules in the gas phase, where simultaneous vibrational and rotational energy changes do occur.

3-1   EXPERIMENTAL METHODS IN INFRARED SPECTRAL REGION

It will be recalled that the infrared region includes radiation that is of longer wavelength, and smaller quantum energy, than that which is detected by the eye. Such radiation is, however, easily detected by its heating effect, and, in this regard, everyone is familiar with the radiation emitted by a hot object. More particularly, infrared heat lamps, which give off little visible radiation but an appreciable amount of infrared, or heat, radiation, are now generally known.

In spectroscopic studies of the vibrations of molecules the spectral region of principal interest is that part of the infrared region which has values of $\bar{\nu}$ between about 100 and 4000 cm^{-1}. In spectroscopy, therefore, it is often customary to call this the infrared region and to use the term "near infrared" for the remaining region, i.e., from $\bar{\nu} = 4000$ cm^{-1} or $\lambda = 25,000$ A to $\lambda = 7500$ A, where the visible region begins.

Radiation in the infrared spectral region is such that optical methods not too different from those described in terms of visible radiation in Sec. 1–2 can be used. Some modifications of the principal components are, however, necessary.

The most characteristic feature of work in this region stems from the fact that glass fails to transmit infrared radiation. (Infrared heat lamps are made with a special glass, and even so they transmit only what we call near-infrared radiation.) The material most generally used for prisms, cells to hold the sample to be placed in the radiation beam, windows, lenses, etc., is rock salt, NaCl. Large single crystals of this material can be grown and are commercially available, and these crystals are cleaved and polished to give the desired optical units. Other salt crystals such as KBr, CsBr, CsI, and

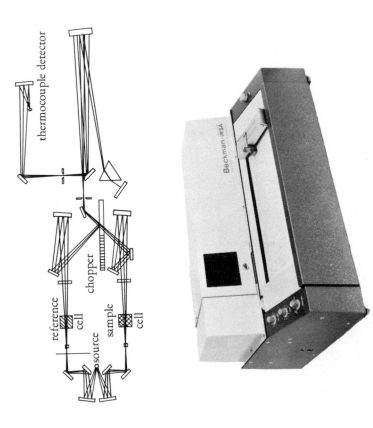

Figure 3–1 The optical arrangement of one of the generally used infrared spectrometers. (Courtesy Beckman Instruments, Inc.)

LiF are also used for special purposes, but rock salt is the transparent material used in most infrared spectroscopy studies. (If one has the opportunity to work in the infrared spectral region, one must remember that the cells are, in fact, made of salt and, unless a very expensive salt solution is desired, water must not be used as a sample or as a solvent!)

The dispersing element most frequently found in an infrared spectrometer is a prism made of rock salt. It should be mentioned, however, that an alternative dispersing element is available and is increasingly found in commercial instruments. Instead of a prism, an appropriately ruled grating can be used. There are some special advantages to the use of gratings; in particular, their use does away with the need for preparing large prisms of materials such as NaCl. Also, since gratings are used as reflection devices, the problems that arise—particularly, far out in the infrared region—with lack of transparency of materials are avoided.

Although a heated tungsten filament, as used in an ordinary light bulb, does give off infrared radiation, it is more satisfactory to use a heated ceramic element as a source of radiation. Such an element is generally heated by means of an electric current until it appears red or even white.

The nature of the detector that is used is governed by the fact that the energy of the quanta in the infrared region is so low that the radiation is not able to eject electrons effectively enough to make a phototube or a photomultiplier operative. One can, however, detect infrared radiation through the heating that occurs when the radiation is absorbed. A very sensitive thermocouple, for example, can be used as a detector.

Finally, the instruments that will be encountered will operate with the double-beam principal, will make use of chopped radiation, and will be so arranged that the absorption spectrum is automatically recorded on chart paper. One of the commercial instruments that operates in the infrared region is illustrated in Fig. 3–1.

3–2   VIBRATION OF
BALL-AND-SPRING SYSTEMS

As in the previous study of the rotation of molecules, it is first desirable to treat systems which behave according to the classical,

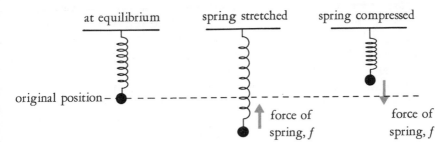

Figure 3–2 The simple vibrating system of a ball and spring showing the displacement from the equilibrium position, and the force f, the restoring force of the spring acting on the ball.

i.e., Newtonian, equations of motion. The way in which molecules vibrate can be approached by considering first the vibrational motion of a single ball attached to a spring, as in Fig. 3–2, and then treating the system consisting of two balls connected by a spring, the counterpart of a diatomic molecule.

Let us first consider the nature of the spring of Fig. 3–2. We shall assume that it behaves, as do many ordinary springs, according to Hooke's law. This law states that the ball, when it is displaced from its equilibrium position by a given amount, experiences a restoring force acting to bring it back to its equilibrium position that is proportional to the amount of the displacement. (Later we shall see that chemical bonds also behave pretty much in accordance with Hooke's law.) If f represents the force of the spring on the particle and x measures the displacement from the equilibrium position, one can write the proportionality equation

$$f \propto x \tag{1}$$

or the equality

$$f = (-k)x. \tag{2}$$

The equality is written with a minus sign shown explicitly so that, although f acts in the direction opposite to that in which x increases, the proportionality constant k will have a positive value. The constant k is known as the *force constant* of the spring. It measures, as is seen by noticing that k is the value of the restoring force for a unit displacement, the stiffness of the spring. A strong, inflexible spring will have a large value of k; a weak, easily extended or compressed spring will have a small value of k.

Now let us consider the motion of the ball attached to the spring. The vibratory motion that we expect implies that the coordinate x that describes the displacement of the ball from its equilibrium position is some repeating function of the time t. If one makes measurements of x at various times t or if one solves the equation that describes the behavior of such systems, one sees that x varies as the sine or the cosine of t according to an equation of the type

$$x = A \sin(\text{const}) \, t \qquad \text{or} \qquad x = A \cos(\text{const}) \, t. \qquad (3)$$

The term A gives the amplitude of the vibration; and, although in some connections it is important, we shall not be concerned with this term here. Either the sine or the cosine function can be used to describe the oscillating motion of the ball. Here we shall proceed with the cosine function.

In discussing the way in which x varies with t it is helpful to look further into the significance of the term written merely as (const) in Eqs. (3). The periodic nature of the motion makes it convenient to write this constant coefficient of t as $2\pi\nu$. When this is done, ν can be identified as a frequency of oscillation, i.e., as the number of vibrations or cycles that the ball makes in 1 sec. One sees this by recognizing that the cosine function completes a cycle every time the argument $2\pi\nu t$ increases by 2π. This occurs every time t increases by $1/\nu$, and it follows that the time interval $1/\nu$ is the number of seconds required for the ball to move through one vibration or cycle. Thus if $1/\nu$ is the number of seconds per cycle, it follows that ν is the number of cycles per second, i.e., the frequency of the vibration.

It now remains to relate the properties of the spring system, i.e., the mass m of the ball and the force constant k of the spring, to the quantity ν, the vibrational frequency in the expression $x = A \cos 2\pi\nu t$ which describes the motion.

The equation to which the motion of the ball must conform is

Newton's $f = ma$ relation. We have already seen that the force on the ball is equal to $-kx$. Furthermore, it will be recalled that the acceleration a is the rate of change of the velocity with respect to time and that the velocity itself is the rate of change of x with respect to time. It follows that the acceleration is the second derivative with respect to time of x and, writing d^2x/dt^2 for a and $-kx$ for f, Newton's equation has the form

$$-kx = m \frac{d^2x}{dt^2}$$

or

$$-\left(\frac{k}{m}\right)x = \frac{d^2x}{dt^2}. \tag{4}$$

One can now readily verify that description of the motion given by $x = A \cos 2\pi\nu t$ satisfies this equation. Substitution for x and for its second derivative gives

$$-\left(\frac{k}{m}\right)A \cos (2\pi\nu t) = -4\pi^2\nu^2 A \cos 2\pi\nu t.$$

The $A \cos 2\pi\nu t$ terms can be canceled and the equality is seen to hold if

$$\frac{k}{m} = 4\pi^2\nu^2$$

or

$$\nu = \frac{1}{2\pi} \sqrt{\frac{k}{m}}. \tag{5}$$

In this way we see that $x = A \cos 2\pi\nu t$ does satisfy Newton's equation and that the vibrational frequency ν is related to the properties, k and m, of the system by Eq. (5). This important classical result implies that for a given spring and mass there is one characteristic, or natural, frequency of vibration and that this frequency can be calculated from Eq. (5). In the following section, where quantum effects are considered, we shall make use of this result; and to emphasize that it is obtained for ordinary-sized systems, we shall then write $\nu_{classical}$ instead of ν. (The energy of the vibrating system would be found to depend on the amplitude A of the oscillating mass. We are, however, not concerned with this aspect.)

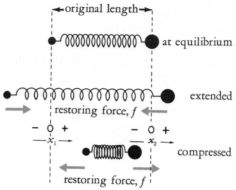

Figure 3–3   The vibrating system of two balls and a spring showing the displacement coordinates x_1 and x_2 and the restoring force f.

The other classical ball-and-spring problem that must be solved in preparation for a study of the vibrations of molecular systems is the spring-and-two-ball arrangement of Fig. 3–3.   One can imagine the balls as lying on a frictionless table or suspended from long cords. The vibrational motion of this dumbbell arrangement can be deduced in a manner analogous to that used for the single-particle system.   One need only notice that the magnitude of the restoring force on each ball depends on the extent of stretching or compression of the spring.   The extension of the spring is given by $x_2 - x_1$, and by comparison with the one-particle system already treated we can write the restoring force as $f = -k(x_2 - x_1)$.   This force acts, as indicated in Fig. 3–3, to move particle 2 to the left when it moves particle 1 to the right.   When care is taken with these different directions, one can substitute the force expression in Newton's $f = ma$ equation for each particle to give the equations

$$+k(x_2 - x_1) = m_1\frac{d^2x_1}{dt^2} \tag{6}$$

and

$$-k(x_2 - x_1) = m_2\frac{d^2x_2}{dt^2}. \tag{7}$$

We can again look for solution functions of the type found for a single particle; and in so doing we try

$$x_1 = A_1 \cos 2\pi\nu t \qquad (8)$$

and

$$x_2 = A_2 \cos 2\pi\nu t, \qquad (9)$$

where the amplitude terms for particles 1 and 2 may be different but the frequency ν must be the same for both particles.

As before, we can relate ν to the properties of the system by substituting these functions back into the equations of motion. We obtain, first,

$$kA_2 \cos 2\pi\nu t - kA_1 \cos 2\pi\nu t = -4\pi^2\nu^2 m_1 A_1 \cos 2\pi\nu t \qquad (10)$$

and

$$-kA_2 \cos 2\pi\nu t + kA_1 \cos 2\pi\nu t = -4\pi^2\nu^2 m_2 A_2 \cos 2\pi\nu t. \qquad (11)$$

The $\cos 2\pi\nu t$ terms can be canceled, and these two equations can be simplified and rearranged to give

$$(-4\pi^2\nu^2 m_1 + k)A_1 = kA_2 \qquad (12)$$

and

$$(-k)A_1 = (4\pi^2\nu^2 m_2 - k)A_2. \qquad (13)$$

Finally, the amplitudes can be eliminated by, for instance, dividing one equation by the other to give, after rearrangement,

$$\frac{4\pi^2\nu^2}{k} = \frac{m_1 + m_2}{m_1 m_2} \qquad (14)$$

or

$$\nu = \frac{1}{2\pi} \sqrt{\frac{k}{\mu}}, \qquad (15)$$

where the reduced mass μ, equal to $m_1 m_2/(m_1 + m_2)$ as introduced in Sec. 2–1, has again been used. With this symbol the expression for the vibration of a two-particle system has the same form as that of Eq. (5) deduced for a one-particle system.

Again we reach the conclusion that the system has a natural

frequency of vibration and that this frequency is related to the force constant and the masses of the system. The amount of energy stored in the vibrations of such a ball-and-spring system would again be found to depend on the amplitude of the vibrational motion.

With this introduction to the vibrational motion of systems that behave classically, we can proceed to see what differences arise when systems of molecular dimensions are encountered and quantum restrictions become important.

3–3 VIBRATIONAL ENERGIES OF DIATOMIC MOLECULES

In more advanced studies of molecular behavior one might proceed directly to solve for the allowed vibrational energies of the molecule by application of Schrödinger's, rather than Newton's, equation. As for the treatment of rotation, one can avoid this procedure and can impose restrictions on the classical results of the preceding section to obtain the allowed vibrational energies.

The way in which the quantum restrictions are introduced into a vibrating system is suggested, in part, by Planck's equation $\Delta \epsilon = h\nu$, which relates the quantum energy to the frequency of the waves of electromagnetic radiation. The allowed vibrational energies of atomic- or molecular-sized systems are given by expressions with a similar form. (The relation $\Delta \epsilon = h\nu$ came, in fact, from Planck's considerations of the vibrational energy of the atoms of a hot object emitting radiation.) Thus the vibrational states that the system is allowed to be in are separated from one another by an energy $\Delta \epsilon_{\mathrm{vib}}$, which is given by the expression

$$\Delta \epsilon_{\mathrm{vib}} = h\nu_{\mathrm{classical}}, \qquad (16)$$

where $\nu_{\mathrm{classical}}$ is the frequency of the natural vibrations that would occur if the system behaved as do ordinary-sized systems. The general expression for the allowed vibrational energies themselves—in contrast to the *spacing* of these levels given by Eq. (16) in molecular-sized systems—is found to be

$$\epsilon_{\mathrm{vib}} = h\nu_{\mathrm{classical}}(v + \tfrac{1}{2}) \qquad v = 0, 1, 2 \ldots . \qquad (17)$$

As for the expression for the allowed rotational energies, an integer appears, here denoted by v. It is called the vibrational quantum number. According to this equation, if the system is in a state described by $v = 0$, it will have a vibrational energy of $\frac{1}{2}h\nu_{\text{classical}}$; if it is in the $v = 1$ state, it will have an energy $\frac{3}{2}h\nu_{\text{classical}}$; if in the $v = 2$ state, it will have an energy $\frac{5}{2}h\nu_{\text{classical}}$; and so forth. One sees that, in spite of the presence of the $\frac{1}{2}$ term in Eq. (17), the allowed vibrational energies are spaced by an amount $h\nu_{\text{classical}}$.

In addition to a restriction on the allowed energies, which we should by now recognize as normal for molecular-dimensioned systems, a second peculiarity now enters. One sees that the lowest vibrational energy that a particle governed by Eq. (17) can have is $\frac{1}{2}h\nu_{\text{classical}}$. This is, of course, in contrast to ordinary-sized systems which are "allowed" to have zero vibrational energy. There are, it should be mentioned, some very interesting consequences of this *zero-point energy* that is retained by all vibrating molecular systems. (At low temperatures, for instance, all the molecules will go into the allowed energy level with the lowest energy. Since there is no allowed energy level at the zero of energy, the molecules cannot get into a zero-energy state.) Thus even at the temperature of absolute zero, vibrating systems will retain some vibrational energy.

For the particular case of a single atomic particle attached by a spring-like chemical bond to a fixed reference point, the expression for the allowed energies is given by Eq. (17) and the expression $\nu_{\text{classical}} = (1/2\pi)\sqrt{k/m}$, which relates $\nu_{\text{classical}}$ to the properties of the particle and the spring. We can write

$$\epsilon_{\text{vib}} = \frac{h}{2\pi}\sqrt{\frac{k}{m}}\,(v + \tfrac{1}{2}) \qquad v = 0, 1, 2, \ldots \qquad (18)$$

In a similar manner the allowed vibrational energies of the chemically more interesting system of a diatomic molecule are given by Eq. (17) and the relation $\nu_{\text{classical}} = (1/2\pi)\sqrt{k/\mu}$ deduced for the classical counterpart of the diatomic molecule. Thus for a diatomic molecule we write

$$\epsilon_{\text{vib}} = \frac{h}{2\pi}\sqrt{\frac{k}{\mu}}\,(v + \tfrac{1}{2}) \qquad v = 0, 1, 2, \ldots \qquad (19)$$

This important result allows us to show diagrammatically the allowed vibrational energies of a diatomic molecule, and this is done schematically in Fig. 3–4. Furthermore, the spectral results to be

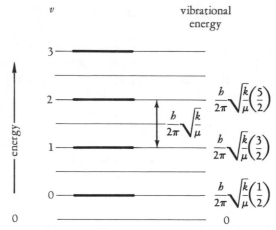

Figure 3-4   The vibrational energies of a diatomic molecule according to the expression $\epsilon_{\text{vib}} = \dfrac{h}{2\pi}\sqrt{\dfrac{k}{\mu}}\,(v + \tfrac{1}{2})$ with $v = 0, 1, 2, \ldots$.

given shortly can here be anticipated to allow the scale diagrams of Fig. 3–5 to be drawn for CO and Cl_2.

These diagrams allow us to compare typical vibrational energy level spacings with our reference energy, the room temperature value of kT. One now finds, in contrast to the situation for rotational energies, that the spacing is large compared to kT. It follows, either from the qualitative discussion of Sec. 1–5 that claimed that few molecules would have an energy much greater than the average classical amount or from application of Boltzmann's expression, that at ordinary temperatures most molecules will have the vibrational energy corresponding to $v = 0$ or, as we say, will be in the $v = 0$ state or energy level.

We now have an expression and diagrams for the allowed vibrational energies, and we know that most molecules of our sample will be in the lowest of these levels. We are in a position, therefore, to understand what happens when infrared radiation, whose quanta

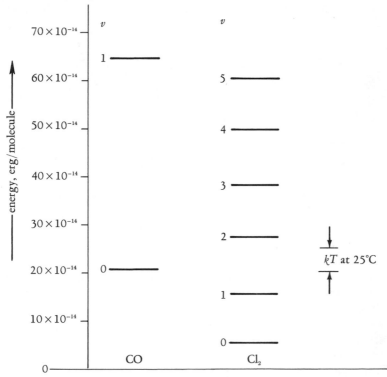

Figure 3–5 The vibrational energies of CO, which are spaced by the relatively large amount of 42×10^{-14} erg, and those energies of Cl_2, which are spaced by the relatively small amount of 11×10^{-14} erg, compared with the value of kT at 25°C.

have energies comparable to the energy spacing of vibrational levels, falls on a sample of diatomic molecules.

3–4 VIBRATIONAL SPECTRA AND FORCE CONSTANTS OF DIATOMIC MOLECULES

Most compounds are found to absorb radiation in the infrared spectral region, and these absorptions can be attributed to changes in

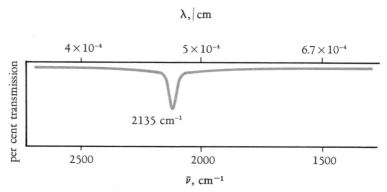

Figure 3–6 The absorption of infrared radiation by CO
molecules showing the absorption band at 2135 cm⁻¹.

the vibrational energy of the absorbing molecule. More specifically, if carbon monoxide is dissolved in the inert solvent carbon tetrachloride, it is found that, as Fig. 3–6 shows, radiation at $\lambda = 0.000468$ cm—or in terms of the frequency units of centimeters⁻¹ usually used in the infrared region, $\bar{\nu} = 2140$ cm⁻¹—is absorbed. At this wavelength the solvent is transparent and the absorption of this radiation must be attributed to the CO molecules in the sample. In similar experiments with other diatomic molecules other absorption bands in this infrared spectral region are observed. We must now ask how the infrared absorption band of a diatomic molecule is related to the energy of the molecules of the sample.

The vibrational energy level diagram of Figs. 3–4 and 3–5 suggests that each molecule might absorb a quantum of radiation and move from the $v = 0$ to $v = 1$ vibrational energy level. The process is indicated by the arrow of Fig. 3–7. If the observed infrared absorption band is attributed to such a transition, the energy spacing of the two vibrational levels can be deduced from the energy of the quanta of the radiation absorbed. For the CO case, for example, the quantum energy of radiation with $\bar{\nu} = 2140$ cm⁻¹, or $\nu = 6.40 \times 10^{13}$ cycles/sec, is

$$\Delta\epsilon = h\nu = 4.24 \times 10^{-13} \text{ erg.} \qquad (20)$$

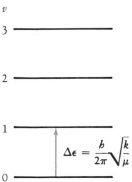

Figure 3–7 The transition from the $v = 0$ to the $v = 1$ vibrational energy level that leads to the absorption of infrared radiation as shown for CO in Fig. 3–6.

Furthermore, the theory of the preceding section tells us that this energy must be equal to the quantity $(h/2\pi)\sqrt{k/\mu}$, where k and μ are, respectively, the force constant and the reduced mass of the molecule absorbing the radiation. For the CO example, for which we deduced in Sec. 2–3 the value of μ to be 1.14×10^{-23} g, we can write

$$4.24 \times 10^{-13} = \frac{h}{2\pi}\sqrt{\frac{k}{\mu}}$$

or

$$k = \frac{4\pi^2(1.14 \times 10^{-23})(4.24 \times 10^{-13})^2}{(6.62 \times 10^{-27})^2}$$

$$= 18.4 \times 10^5 \text{ dyne/cm.}$$

Thus, when the infrared absorption band corresponding to the vibrational transition from $v = 0$ to $v = 1$ can be identified, its frequency, called the *fundamental frequency*, can be used to deduce a value for the force constant of the bond of the molecule. In a similar way the infrared absorption bands of other diatomic molecules can be used to obtain bond force constants. Some results are listed in Table 3–1.

Structures of Molecules

Table 3-1

The Positions of the Fundamental Vibrational Absorptions of Some Diatomic Molecules and the Bond Force Constants Deduced from These Values

Molecule	$\bar{v}, cm^{-1}$, for the $v = 0$ to $v = 1$ absorption band	Force constant, dynes/cm
HF	2907	9.7×10^5
HCl	2886	4.8×10^5
HBr	2559	4.1×10^5
HI	2230	3.2×10^5
CO	2143	18.4×10^5
NO	1876	15.3×10^5

It should be recognized that the deduction of the stiffness of a chemical bond, which is the quantity measured by the force constant, is a rather impressive feat. An appreciation of the results is, perhaps, most easily reached by comparing the variation in the stiffness of different molecules. One notices, for example, the great rigidity of the HF molecule as compared to the HI molecule. Similarly, the multiple-bonded CO molecule shows a greater rigidity than the single-bond molecules.

3–5   AMPLITUDE OF MOLECULAR VIBRATIONS

One can also attempt to appreciate the degree of stiffness, or flexibility, of molecules by investigating the amplitude of their vibrations when, for example, they have the energy corresponding to the $v = 0$ level. This can be done in a simple, but not entirely correct, manner by resorting to some extent to the classical picture of a vibrating system. With this view one can recognize that at the limits of a vibration, as the particles are turning around to reverse their direction, there is no kinetic energy and all the energy of the system must be potential energy. For the molecular case and the $v = 0$ level we can ask how much the bond will stretch if the energy of this level is used up in increasing the potential energy. The potential-energy increase that accompanies bond stretching can be calculated as stored work. If the bond is to be stretched to an extension x, a force must be exerted in opposition to that of the spring. We can perform the necessary integration to give the potential energy of the system as a function of the displacement from the equilibrium position as

$$\text{increase in PE} = \int_0^x kx\,dx = \frac{kx^2}{2}\Big]_0^x,$$

whence

$$\text{increase in PE} = \tfrac{1}{2}kx^2. \tag{21}$$

This general result can be applied to find the maximum displacement, i.e., the amplitude for the $v = 0$ state. The potential energy at $x = x_{\text{max}}$ is equal to the total energy of the $v = 0$ state, and one writes

$$\frac{1}{2}\left(\frac{h}{2\pi}\right)\sqrt{\frac{k}{\mu}} = \frac{1}{2}kx_{\text{max}}^2 \tag{22}$$

For HCl, for example, one has from Table 3–1, $k = 4.8 \times 10^5$ dynes/cm and with $\mu = 1.61 \times 10^{-24}$ g one can calculate

$$\text{amplitude of vibration} = 0.11 \times 10^{-8}\text{ cm} = 0.11\text{ A}. \tag{23}$$

When this result is compared with the equilibrium bond length of 1.27×10^{-8} cm, or 1.27 A, obtained by the methods of the preceding chapter, one sees that the vibrational amplitude is about 10 per cent of the bond length. This calculation shows that molecules are not to be thought of as rigid structures even in the lowest allowed vibrational state. They, in fact, compare with rather flexible spring systems.

3–6 MECHANISM OF INFRARED-RADIATION ABSORPTION

Now that we see that molecular properties can be deduced from an identification of the infrared absorption band of a diatomic molecule with the $v = 0$ to $v = 1$ vibrational transition, we can go back and comment on the way in which the transfer of energy between the radiation and the molecule occurs. The mechanism is very similar to that discussed in connection with rotational transitions.

We again ask if the electric field of the radiation can interact with a vibrating molecule to cause it to jump from its initial $v = 0$ level to the higher $v = 1$ level. Such interaction can be accounted for if it is supposed that the molecule has positively and negatively charged ends and that the amount of charge on the ends varies with the internuclear distance. If such is the case, the molecule might have a larger (or smaller) dipole moment in the stretched configuration than it has in the compressed configuration. It follows that the magnitude of the charges on the ends of the molecule will oscillate as the molecule vibrates. These oscillating charges can be in phase with the electric field of the radiation, so that for each vibration the field pushes the molecule to vibrate more if the radiation field has the same frequency as that of the molecular vibration. We see that the same type of mechanism acts in the vibrating molecule as in the rotating molecule to allow the radiation to transfer energy to the molecule. For this to occur for vibrational energies, the molecule must have an oscillating dipole moment. The dipole moments of heteronuclear molecules such as CO and HCl can generally be expected to be a function of the internuclear distance, and such molecules can therefore absorb infrared radiation and go from the $v = 0$ to $v = 1$ state. On the other hand, homonuclear diatomic molecules such as H_2 and N_2 have no dipole moment no matter what the internuclear distance is. It follows that, as for rotation, they cannot interact with radiation to change their vibrational energy. Such molecules are in fact found to have no absorption band in the infrared spectral region.

As for rotational energy changes, a further restriction limits the vibrational change that a molecule makes as a result of interaction with radiation to a jump to the next higher or next lower allowed vibrational energy. The selection rule is, therefore, $\Delta v = \pm 1$. If the molecules are originally in the $v = 0$ state or if only absorption of radiation is considered, the $\Delta v = +1$ part of the selection rule is pertinent. (It should, however, be pointed out that this selection rule is based on the assumption that the chemical bond behaves exactly like a Hooke's law spring. We shall see that this is not quite so and, as a consequence, one can often observe very weak absorption bands corresponding to "overtone" transitions from the $v = 0$ level to $v = 2, 3, \ldots$ levels in violation of the selection rule $\Delta v = \pm 1$.)

Although a few of the finer details of the vibrations of diatomic molecules remain to be mentioned, let us now proceed to see what happens, and what we can learn, when the molecules in the beam of infrared radiation are polyatomic molecules.

3-7 VIBRATIONAL SPECTRA
OF POLYATOMIC MOLECULES

The single vibrational motion, or degree of freedom, of a diatomic molecule leads to the single principal absorption band observed, if the molecule has an oscillating dipole moment, in the infrared spectral region. For polyatomic molecules, as we have seen, there will be $3n - 6$ ($3n - 5$ for linear molecules) basic ways in which the molecule can vibrate. This number of vibrational modes can lead to a corresponding number of vibrational energy patterns, each like that of Fig. 3-4. It follows, and the spectra of Fig. 3-8 bear this out, that there will be a correspondingly greater number of $v = 0$ to $v = 1$ transitions and thus a more complicated infrared spectrum.

The molecule H_2O, for example, has, according to the $3n - 6$ expression, three basic or *natural* vibrations. Each of these vibrations can be treated as was the single vibration of a diatomic molecule, and each therefore leads to a diagram representing the allowed energies that the molecule can have as a result of vibrating with that natural way. The experimental spectrum for H_2O dissolved in an inert solvent, given in Fig. 3-8, shows three dominant absorptions. Each of the three absorption bands in the spectrum allows us to deduce the energy spacing between the $v = 0$ and $v = 1$ levels of one of the patterns. With this information we can draw the three vibrational energy level diagrams for H_2O as in Fig. 3-9.

If we were to follow the procedure used for diatomic molecules, we would now deduce information on the flexibility of the molecule from these energy spacings. This step is, however, one of appreciable difficulty for polyatomic molecules. It would be necessary to determine how the molecule vibrates, i.e., how the atoms move

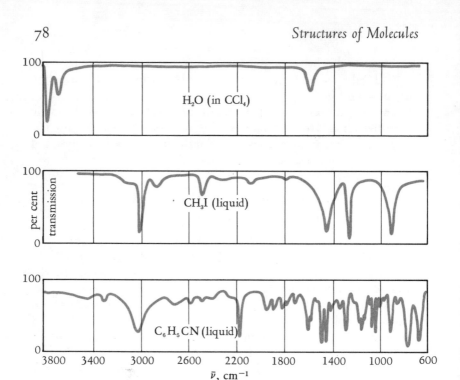

per cent transmission

H_2O (in CCl_4)

CH_3I (liquid)

C_6H_5CN (liquid)

3800   3400   3000   2600   2200   1800   1400   1000   600

$\bar{\nu}$, cm^{-1}

Figure 3–8 The increasing number of absorption bands generally found in the infrared spectrum of molecules with increasing numbers of atoms. (The observed absorption bands correspond to some of the $3n$-6 vibrations and to some combinations and overtones of these.)

relative to one another, in each of the natural vibrations. This can be done for small molecules but becomes increasingly difficult when there are many, say more than a dozen, vibrations. An approximate, but very useful, description of the vibrations of a molecule can, however, be given. With this procedure one associates a bond-stretching vibration, comparable to that of diatomic molecules, with each bond of the molecule and an angle-bending vibration with each angle between chemical bonds. With this view one can associate, in the H_2O example, the two higher-frequency bands with stretching vi-

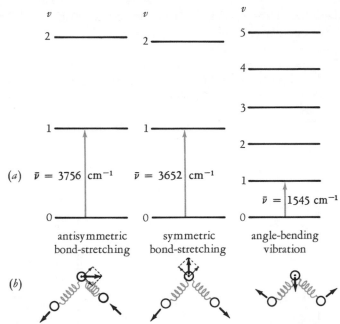

Figure 3-9 (*a*) The three vibrational energy-level diagrams for the H_2O molecule that can be deduced from the infrared absorption spectrum of Fig. 3–8. In (*b*) is shown the way in which the atoms would have to be moved so that, when released, the corresponding vibration would occur.

brations of the two O—H bonds and the different, lower-frequency band with the bending motion. One should recognize that vibrations that are essentially the angle-bending type can occur in just the same way that bond-stretching vibrations occur. Just as a bond-stretching type of vibration can be generated by stretching the bonds of a model, as shown at the bottom of Fig. 3–9, so also, if the balls representing the atoms are displaced so that the bond angle is changed from its equilibrium value, a vibration that would be called a bending vibration or a bending mode will result.

The identification of an absorption band with a stretching or bending vibrational mode is a procedure often used to qualitatively describe infrared absorptions of large molecules. Some of the motions that are often recognized and that have rather fixed absorption frequencies are shown in Fig. 3–10.

The question why, since the two O—H bonds of H_2O are identical, the two stretching vibrations lead to absorption of radiation with slightly different frequencies might arise. Here it can only be

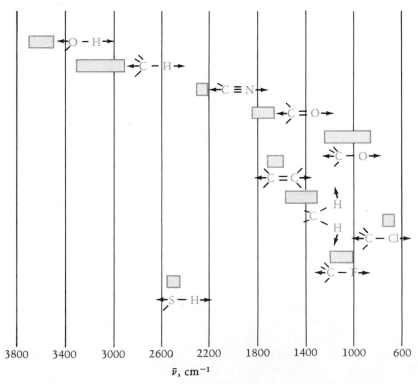

Figure 3–10   The frequency range within which absorption bands characteristic of certain groups of atoms are found. The nature of the vibration giving rise to the band is also shown. Much more extensive tables of characteristic absorptions are available.

mentioned that each absorption is not to be attributed to a separate vibration of each bond. Rather, as shown in Fig. 3–9, the vibrations of the two bonds are coupled to give a symmetric stretching vibration and an antisymmetric stretching vibration. These two motions correspond to natural vibrations, and it is such motions that are to be matched up with the two absorption bands near $\bar{v} = 3700$ cm^{-1}. One will find, if one proceeds with the study of molecular vibrations, that the symmetry of the molecule and the symmetry of the vibrations are very important and often allow rather complicated vibrational spectra to be understood.

A further result that can be obtained from the recognition of angle-bending and bond-stretching motions are the force constants for such motions. The general conclusion, which is of considerable chemical significance, that can be drawn from these results is that angles are much more easily deformed than are bonds. The fact that the energy level spacings for the stretching motions of the H_2O molecule are much greater than for the bending motion illustrates, in view of the general dependence of the $v = 0$ to $v = 1$ spacing on the force constant indicated in Fig. 3–4, the general rule that bond-stretching force constants are considerably greater than angle-bending force constants.

We shall not proceed further with a discussion of the vibrational spectra of polyatomic molecules. In more advanced work it will be found that very detailed information on the relative ease with which various distortions can be imposed on the molecule can be obtained. Furthermore, it will be found that the infrared absorption spectrum of a sample is an invaluable aid to the identification and characterization of the molecules of the sample. In view of the summary of characteristic absorption frequencies given in Fig. 3–10, for example, the occurrence of an absorption band at a frequency $\bar{v}$ of about 1700 cm^{-1} indicates the presence of a $C{=}O$ group in the molecules of the sample. Similarly, the infrared spectrum of a sample would reveal the presence of a number of groups and, if the sample were an unknown, would aid in its identification. Much more extensive correlations of atomic groups and characteristic absorption bands than that given in Fig. 3–10 are available, and with such information the identification of both organic and inorganic compounds is greatly aided.

3–8   POTENTIAL-ENERGY FUNCTION FOR

A CHEMICAL BOND

One further aspect of the behavior of diatomic molecules should be treated before we move on to another subject. The student is probably already familiar with the fact that we can talk either of particles attached by springs being returned to their equilibrium position by the action of a restoring force or of the tendency of the particles to return to this position to be a result of the system moving to a position of lower potential energy. Although in the introduction given here to vibrations of systems the former view has been used, in more advanced work the latter, potential-energy view is usually more convenient. Let us therefore investigate the way in which the potential energy of a diatomic molecule varies with the internuclear distance.

The assumption that for not too large distortions a bond behaves according to Hooke's law implies that the potential energy rises parabolically from a minimum at the equilibrium position. We see this by calculating, as we did to obtain the vibrational amplitude, the work stored by the bond when it is distorted from its equilibrium position. If the potential energy for the equilibrium bond length is taken to be zero, one obtains the potential energy for other bond lengths by integrating the force kx over the distortion distances dx to obtain

$$\text{PE} = \int_0^x kx \, dx = \tfrac{1}{2}kx^2, \tag{24}$$

where x is the displacement from the equilibrium position. This potential function is equivalent to the Hooke's law restoring force statement. Since this behavior leads to the allowed vibrational energies for a diatomic molecule given by Eq. (19), one often indicates the potential-energy curve and the allowed vibrational energies on the same diagram, as is done in Fig. 3–11.

The potential-energy curve of Fig. 3–11 can, however, apply only near the equilibrium position. One knows, for example, that if the bond is stretched to, say, 2 or 3 times its normal length, it will be pretty well destroyed and further extensions will be relatively easy. This implies that for large extensions the restoring force will

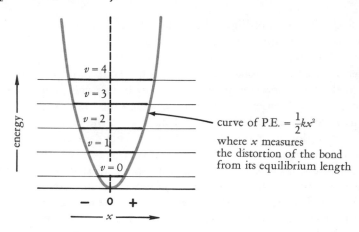

$v = 4$

$v = 3$

$v = 2$

curve of P.E. $= \frac{1}{2}kx^2$

$v = 1$

where x measures
the distortion of the bond
from its equilibrium length

$v = 0$

energy

$-$ 0 $+$

x

Figure 3–11 The potential-energy curve and the allowed-vibrational-energy levels for a diatomic molecule on the basis of Hooke's law behavior.

no longer increase proportionally to the extension but will in fact decrease and, for infinite separation, become zero. In terms of the potential-energy function for the bond this implies that the potential energy does not continue to rise parabolically, but rather rises more and more slowly as the bond length increases until, at very great lengths, the potential energy does not increase with further extension. At the other extreme, where the bond is greatly compressed, the repulsion of the nuclei, through their relatively large nuclear charges, and the repulsion of the many electrons of the two atoms will become very dominant factors and the bond will strongly resist further bond shortening. It follows that at these short bond lengths the potential energy will rise very steeply. These arguments, and other more quantitative ones that can be given, lead to a more complete potential curve of the shape shown in Fig. 3–12. A dashed Hooke's law potential curve is also included to show that for small distortions this is an adequate approximation.

A very careful study of the vibrational spectra of molecules requires one to recognize that Hooke's law is, in fact, only an approximation and that the more complete potential-energy curve has the shape indicated in Fig. 3–12. The vibrational energies that are allowed to a diatomic molecule whose nuclei are attached by a "spring" showing this potential function can be calculated. The lower allowed vibrational energy levels turn out to be spaced very much like those obtained previously. The higher energy levels are, as might have been expected from the fact that the motion of the atoms is less restricted than would have been the case if Hooke's law were followed, more closely spaced. This deviation from the constant spacing of allowed vibrational energies shows up in positions of the weak absorptions that correspond to transitions of the type $v = 0$ to $v = 2$, $v = 0$ to $v = 3$, and so forth. As Table 3–2 shows, for HCl these *overtone* transitions have quantum energies that are all somewhat less than integral multiples of the quantum energies of the fundamental $v = 0$ to $v = 1$ transition. In practice, use can be made of the spectroscopically measured spacings of the vibrational energy levels to construct the potential-energy curve for the molecule. One must remember, however, that the variation from

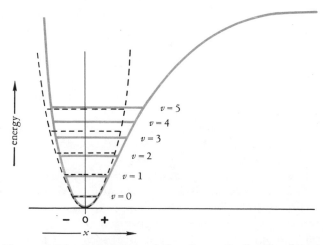

Figure 3–12 Comparison of the observed vibrational energies and corresponding potential-energy curve with those deduced on the basis of Hooke's law.

Table 3-2

The Frequencies, in centimeters^{-1}, of the Fundamental $v = 0$ to $v = 1$ Transition and Several Overtones of HCl

Transition	$\bar{v}, cm^{-1}$ (observed)	$\bar{v}, cm^{-1}$ (calculated from multiples of $v = 0 \rightarrow v = 1$ frequency)
$v = 0 \rightarrow v = 1$	2,886	(2,886)
$v = 0 \rightarrow v = 2$	5,668	5,772
$v = 0 \rightarrow v = 3$	8,347	8,658
$v = 0 \rightarrow v = 4$	10,923	11,544

Hooke's law is sufficiently small in the lower part of the curve that the previous results for the force constants of molecules are still very reliable.

SUMMARY

The absorption of radiation in the infrared region is attributed to the absorption of quanta of radiation by the molecules of the sample in such a way that the molecules increase the energy with which they vibrate. The frequencies of the infrared radiation that are absorbed are those that correspond to quantum energies that are just right to raise the vibrational energy of a molecule from one allowed value to another. Measurement of the infrared absorption spectrum of a material therefore gives information on the spacings of the allowed vibrational energies.

The spacing of the vibrational energy levels of a molecule is related to the rigidity of the molecule, i.e., to the stiffness of the bonds and the angles between the bonds of the molecule. The force constants of the molecule, which measure the stiffness or flexibility of the molecule, are deduced from the information provided by the infrared absorption spectrum.

Many studies continue to be made in attempts to obtain force constants for all the bonds and bond angles of polyatomic molecules from infrared absorption spectra. As in the analysis of the microwave spectra of such molecules, the interpretation of the large amount of data given by the frequencies at which radiation is absorbed cannot easily be made. Only for relatively small molecules, such as the H_2O molecule, can the task be adequately performed with theoretical methods currently available. Future developments, probably making use of modern computing techniques, will undoubtedly provide methods for handling many more of the molecules whose special rigidity or flexibility is of interest to chemists.

Most of this chapter has, like most actual studies of molecular vibrations, been concerned with the frequencies of the radiation that are absorbed by vibrating molecules. More recently, some attention has been given to the relation between the amount of radiation absorbed by a particular sample and the properties of the molecules of the sample. As suggested by the discussion of Sec. 3–5, one learns from such studies about the way in which the dipole moment of the molecule, i.e., the amount to which one end of the molecule is more or less negatively or positively charged than the other end, varies as the molecule vibrates. In general, we expect the dipole moment to depend on the internuclear distances in the molecule because, as the molecule is distorted from its equilibrium configuration during a vibration, the arrangement of the electrons in the molecule will change. It seems certain that much future work will be directed toward measurements of amounts of absorption by vibrating molecules and the deduction from these data of information on how the electronic distribution in a molecule changes as the molecule vibrates. In this way some of the most intimate details of the phenomena that occur within a molecule will be made available to the chemist.

EXERCISES

1. Calculate the natural frequency with which a ball of mass 10 g would vibrate if it were attached to a spring with a force constant of 1000 dyne/cm. What would be the frequency if the spring were 10 times stronger? If it were 10 times weaker? What would be the frequency of vibration if the mass attached to the original 1000-dyne/cm spring were 1 g instead of 10 g? If it were 100 g instead of 10 g? Summarize the above results by a statement regarding the dependence of the frequency of vibration on the force constant and the mass of the vibrating system.

(*Ans.:* $v = 1.59$ *cycles/sec*)

2. Calculate the natural frequency of a system like that dealt with in Exercise 1 of Chap. 2, that is, balls of mass 1 g and 2 g separated by a distance of 10 cm. Now assume that the balls are held at this distance by a spring that resists extension or compression with a force constant of 100 dyne/cm.

(*Ans.:* $v = 1.95$ *cycles/sec*)

3. Using the energy level spacings from Fig. 3–4, calculate the number of molecules that have $v = 1$ relative to the number that have $v = 0$ for CO at 25°C. Repeat the calculation for 1000°C.

(*Ans.:* At 25°C, $n_1/n_0 = 3 \times 10^{-5}$; at 1000°C $n_1/n_0 = 0.09$)

4. Referring to Figs. 1–4 and 3–4, see that the energy spacing between allowed vibrational energy levels is comparable with the energy of quanta of infrared radiation.

5. For HCl calculate the frequency, in cycles per second, and the quantum energy, in ergs, corresponding to the frequency of 2886 cm^{-1} of the radiation absorbed in the fundamental vibrational transition. Calculate the reduced mass of HCl and then verify the value of the force constant given in Table 3–1.

6. Assume that the force constant for DCl is the same as that for HCl and calculate the frequency, in centimeters^{-1}, of the infrared radiation that will be absorbed by DCl. Compare with the observed absorption frequency of about 2100 cm^{-1}. (Note from this the general rule that replacement of H by D lowers the stretching frequency by approximately a factor of $\sqrt{2}$.)

7. Calculate the amplitude of the vibrations in the $v = 0$ level of the molecule CO, which has a rather stiff bond, and HI, which has a rather weak bond.

(*Ans.:* For CO, $x_{max} = 0.05$ A; for HI, $x_{max} = 0.12$ A)

8. Using the force constant of 9.7×10^5 dyne/cm and the reduced mass of 1.58×10^{-24} g for HF: (a) Plot the potential-energy vs. internuclear-distance curve near the equilibrium distance of 0.92 A; (b) Add the allowed vibrational energies as horizontal lines to the diagram.

9. Using the same scale as that used in Exercise 8, plot the potential-energy curve and the allowed vibrational energies for HI

for which the force constant is 3.2×10^5 dynes/cm, the reduced mass is 1.64×10^{-24}, and the equilibrium internuclear distance is 1.60 A. Compare the figure obtained in Exercise 8 for HF with the figure obtained here for HI and see that this comparison illustrates the general rule that when the motion of a system is more restricted, the quantum restrictions are more important, i.e., the steps between the allowed energies are greater.

IV

The Simultaneous Rotation and Vibration of Diatomic Molecules

Although in the preceding two chapters the principal information that can be obtained from studies of the rotational and the vibrational spectra of simple molecules has been pointed out, it is perhaps of some interest to show how the spectra of molecules that are both rotating and vibrating can be understood. The student may, in fact, have more of an opportunity to see the spectral effects of molecular rotation in what is called the vibration-rotation spectrum. Such effects appear in the infrared spectral region, and many more laboratories are equipped with instruments that operate in this area than in the microwave region.

4-1 ENERGIES OF VIBRATING
AND ROTATING MOLECULES

Any diatomic or polyatomic molecule in the gas phase can, as discussed in Chap. 1, have energy because of both rotational and vibrational motion. The behavior of diatomic gas-phase molecules with which we shall be concerned here can pretty well be accounted for by adding together the expressions obtained in the preceding two chapters for the separate rotations and vibrations of molecules. In terms of the formulas deduced previously for the allowed energies one can write for a gas-phase diatomic molecule

$$\epsilon_{\text{rot-vib}} = \frac{h^2}{8\pi^2 I} J(J + 1) + \frac{h}{2\pi} \sqrt{\frac{k}{\mu}} (v + \tfrac{1}{2}) \qquad \begin{array}{l} J = 0, 1, 2, \ldots \\[8pt] v = 0, 1, 2, \ldots \end{array} \tag{1}$$

As in the preceding chapter, much of our present interest is connected with the $v = 0$ and the $v = 1$ vibrational states. In fact, the rotational energies of molecules in the $v = 0$ state have already been dealt with in Chap. 2. There nothing was said about the vibrations of the molecule, but now we know that the molecules studied were really in the lowest, $v = 0$, vibrational state and had the half unit of vibrational energy that such molecules must have.

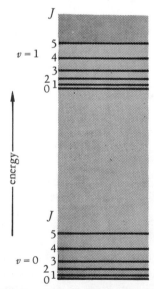

Figure 4–1 The allowed-energy-level pattern for a rotating-vibrating diatomic molecule. (Only the first two vibrational levels and first five rotational levels are shown.)

Furthermore, if a molecule is in the $v = 1$ vibrational level, it also can rotate and, to a pretty good approximation, its allowed rotational energies will form the same pattern as for the $v = 0$ state molecule. The allowed simultaneous vibrational and rotational energies are given by inserting the appropriate values of v and J in Eq. (1). These are also shown diagrammatically in Fig. 4-1.

We are now in a position to investigate the transitions that can occur when a gaseous sample is exposed to infrared radiation and the molecules of the sample, which originally are distributed throughout many of the rotational levels of the $v = 0$ state, absorb energy and go to certain of the rotational levels of the $v = 1$ state.

4-2 ROTATION-VIBRATION SPECTRUM OF GASEOUS DIATOMIC MOLECULES

In preparation for a study of the infrared absorption spectrum of a gas-phase sample of diatomic molecules we shall now draw in, on a diagram showing the allowed rotation and vibration energies, the arrows that correspond to the possible transitions from the $v = 0$ to the $v = 1$ state. In contrast to the single arrow that was drawn in the preceding chapter for nonrotating molecules, now many arrows can be drawn from the various occupied rotational levels of the $v = 0$ state to various rotational levels of the $v = 1$ state. The selection rule stated for rotational transitions, that $\Delta J = \pm 1$, still holds, and only those arrows that connect levels such that this rule is obeyed are drawn.

It is helpful to space the arrows horizontally so that the shortest one, corresponding to the absorption of the smallest quantum of energy, is on the right while to the left is the longest arrow corresponding to the transition absorbing the largest quantum. This is done in Fig. 4-2. The pattern of arrows is easily constructed if one starts at the center where the $v = 0$ to $v = 1$ transition with $\Delta J = 0$ would be if it were allowed. This forbidden transition is indicated by the dashed line of Fig. 4-2. Now one works out to the left drawing arrows from levels with a given value of J in the $v = 0$ state to levels with one higher value of J in the $v = 1$ state. Similarly, one works out to the right drawing arrows from levels with a given value of J in the $v = 0$ state to levels with one lower value of

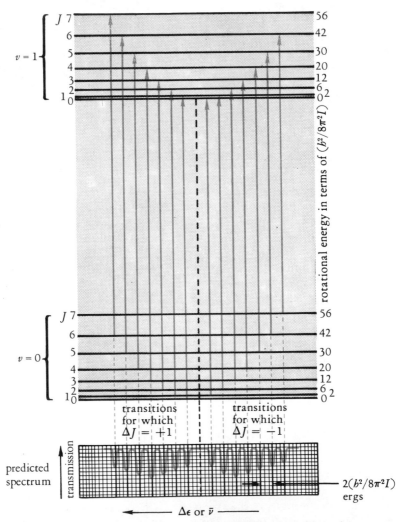

Figure 4–2 Some of the rotation-vibration transitions for a gas-phase diatomic molecule. The absorption spectrum that these transitions would produce is shown in the lower portion of the illustration.

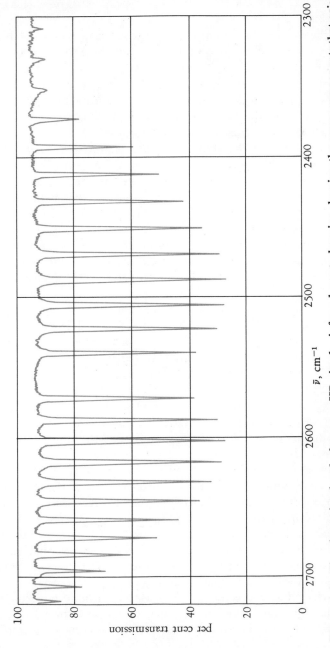

Figure 4-3 The absorption band of gaseous HBr in the infrared spectral region showing the many components that arise as a result of simultaneous changes in the vibrational and rotational energy of the molecule.

J in the $v = 1$ state. If one keeps track of the increases and decreases in the lengths of the arrows by means of the energy scale in terms of $h^2/8\pi^2 I$, one finds, as inspection of Fig. 4–2 shows, that there is a gap in the center where the $\Delta J = 0$ arrows would have been and that the $\Delta J = +1$ arrows form a pattern with a spacing $2(h^2/8\pi^2 I)$ to the left and the $\Delta J = -1$ arrows form a corresponding pattern to the right, also with a spacing $2(h^2/8\pi^2 I)$.

According to the above analysis, quanta with energies corresponding to the lengths of the arrows of Fig. 4–2 will be absorbed when the infrared absorption spectrum of gas-phase diatomic molecules is obtained. It is customary to indicate the predicted absorption spectrum underneath the set of arrows that have just been drawn. We have arranged the arrows in such a way that if we· simply drop perpendiculars to an energy scale, or in view of the relation $\Delta \epsilon = h\nu$ to a frequency scale, we get the predicted pattern for the vibration-rotation absorption band. This is also shown in Fig. 4–2.

The infrared absorption band of HBr gas is shown in Fig. 4–3. The expectations as to the effect of rotation discussed above and predicted in Fig. 4–2 can be seen to be nicely borne out by the positions of the many components of the band.

As in the analyses given in the preceding two chapters, once the expected spectral pattern is observed, the measured positions, or spacings, of the absorptions can be used to determine molecular properties. The principal quantities that characterize a spectrum such as that of Fig. 4–3 are the frequency of the band center, which corresponds to a $v = 0$ to $v = 1$ transition with no accompanying change in rotational energy, and the spacing of the rotational components within the band. As discussed in Chap. 3, the first measured quantity allows calculation of the bond force constant, while as discussed in Chap. 2, the second quantity allows calculation of the moment of inertia and the equilibrium bond length. Thus, studies of the infrared absorption bands of gases yield information on the structure as well as the rigidity of molecules without recourse to the experimentally less convenient microwave spectroscopy.

The infrared spectra of gas-phase polyatomic molecules show similar rotational structure in each of the vibrational absorption bands. The spectra of such molecules can become very rich in de-

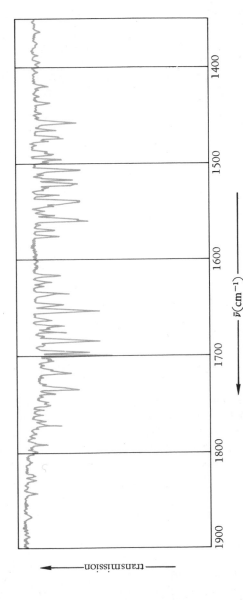

Figure 4-4 The absorption band due to the bending vibration (and simultaneous rotational changes), of the asymmetric-top molecule H_2O. The position of the band center is related to the force constants and the atomic masses. The positions and intensities of the many components are related to the moments of inertia and dipole moment of the molecule.

95

tail, and we shall leave the analyses of such spectra to more advanced studies. Just to indicate the complexity that can arise in such spectra, Fig. 4–4 shows the infrared absorption spectrum of H_2O vapor. Since H_2O is an asymmetric-top molecule, i.e., its three principal moments of inertia are of different magnitudes, the patterns of allowed rotational energies in both the $v = 0$ state and the $v = 1$ state are very complicated. It follows that the transitions between the rotational levels accompanying the fundamental vibrational transitions will form correspondingly complicated bands. Only in a few cases has it been possible to understand completely such complicated vibration-rotation spectra in terms of molecular energies and then to deduce properties of the molecule from such spectra.

4–3   RELATIVE COMPONENT INTENSITIES OF A ROTATION-VIBRATION ABSORPTION BAND

If one looks carefully at the actual absorption band of Fig. 4–3, one perhaps notices two features that have so far not been discussed. These are the variation in the amount of radiation absorbed, i.e., in the intensity of the components of the band, and the fact that the spacing between the components is not, in fact, exactly constant throughout the band. Let us now treat the first of these two finer details of the rotation-vibration spectrum.

The variation in intensity of the components of the rotation-vibration band can be understood by considering the relative numbers of molecules that are in the various rotational states of the $v = 0$ level. The relative populations of these states will determine the relative intensities of the components of the rotation-vibration band. One additional feature, beyond the Boltzmann distribution, must be introduced to obtain the necessary populations.

This feature can be made evident by imagining the rotating molecule to be in an electric field which tries to line up the molecule in the direction of the field. The presence of the field reveals further quantum restrictions beyond that requiring the total angular momentum to be given by $\sqrt{J(J + 1)}(h/2\pi)$. Now, not only must the total angular momentum be quantized but so also must be the component in the direction of the field. This added restriction states that the angular-momentum component in the direction of the field must have one of the values

$$J\left(\frac{h}{2\pi}\right), (J-1)\frac{h}{2\pi}, \ldots, 0, -\frac{h}{2\pi}, \ldots, -J\frac{h}{2\pi}.$$

Thus if $J = 2$, the component of the angular momentum in the direction of the applied field must be

$$2\left(\frac{h}{2\pi}\right), \frac{h}{2\pi}, 0, -\frac{h}{2\pi}, \text{ or } -2\left(\frac{h}{2\pi}\right).$$

These restrictions are often illustrated by representing the total angular momentum by a vector of length $\sqrt{J(J+1)}(h/2\pi)$ units and orienting this vector in space to give the allowed components along the given direction. Such a diagram is shown for the rotation level with $J = 2$ in Fig. 4-5. One recognizes that the electric field would split the original $J = 2$ rotational state into five states differing with regard to their orientation relative to the field. They would, furthermore, correspond to different energies as a result of their different orientations with respect to the field.

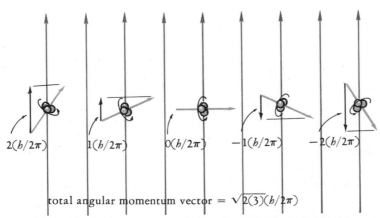

$2(h/2\pi)$ $1(h/2\pi)$ $0(h/2\pi)$ $-1(h/2\pi)$ $-2(h/2\pi)$

total angular momentum vector $= \sqrt{2(3)}(h/2\pi)$

Figure 4-5 The allowed orientations of a rotating molecule with $J = 2$ in an electric field. The molecule must rotate in a direction relative to the field, so that its angular momentum in this direction is an integral multiple of $h/2\pi$.

If the field is now imagined to be gradually reduced to zero, at no point will any of these states suddenly disappear. The energies of these states will, rather, coalesce to the one rotational energy level that we have been treating for free, rotating molecules. The behavior in the presence of the field is important in that it reveals that for each allowed rotational energy there are really a number of different states. For the energy level corresponding to the rotational quantum number J, one can easily check that the quantum restrictions on the component in the direction of the field reveals $2J + 1$ states. We say that the Jth energy level has a *multiplicity of $2J + 1$*, or that it is *($2J + 1$)-fold degenerate.*

This multiplicity is important because the Boltzmann distribution gives us the number of molecules *per state;* and if there are $2J + 1$ states with a given energy, there will be $2J + 1$ times as many molecules with that energy as there would have been if there were a single state. We can write Boltzmann's distribution to give us the number of molecules in the J energy level, rather than in each state with this energy, by including the multiplicity factor and writing

$$\frac{n_J}{n_0} = (2J + 1)e^{-(\epsilon_J - \epsilon_0)/kT}. \tag{2}$$

This expression leads, for increasing values of J, to an initial increase in population because the $2J + 1$ term increases and the exponential term remains near unity. However, at high J values the energy term $\epsilon_J - \epsilon_0$ becomes large and the exponential decreases faster than the $2J + 1$ coefficient increases. These two factors so operate that Eq. (2) leads to the population of the rotational levels for our example of HBr at 25°C as shown in Fig. 4–6. `

The probability that a particular frequency of radiation will be absorbed, and will give rise to one of the components of the rotation-vibration band, is approxmiately proportional to the number of molecules that are present in the gas sample and have the initial rotational energy that gives rise to the component. The intensities of the rotational components of the rotation-vibration band are therefore proportional to the populations of the rotational energy levels in the ground vibrational state. Thus the population distribution of Fig. 4–6 carries over into the intensity variation of the components of Fig. 4–3. We now, therefore, have reached an

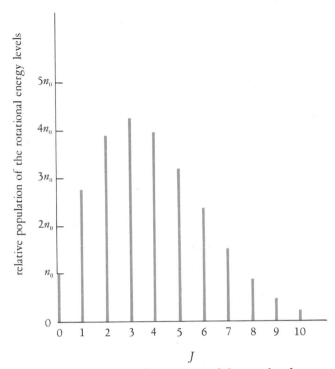

Figure 4-6 **The populations of some of the rotational-energy levels of HBr at 25°C in terms of n_0, the number of molecules in the $J = 0$ level.**

understanding of the variation in intensity of the components of the rotation-vibration bands of gas-phase diatomic molecules.

4-4 ASYMMETRY OF A ROTATION-VIBRATION ABSORPTION BAND

Now let us proceed to the second feature and ask why the spacing between the components diverges from the constant value expected from our simple theoretical deduction and what molecular property can be deduced from an analysis of this finer detail.

The weakness in the treatment of the allowed vibration-rotation energy levels that has led to this failure to account for the observation is the assumption that the moments of inertia in the $v = 0$ and $v = 1$ vibrational states are the same. In view of the shape of the potential-energy curve of Fig. 3–12, in particular the fact that it tends to spread out to larger internuclear distances at higher energies, one can expect that when the molecule vibrates with energy corresponding to $v = 1$, it will have an effectively longer bond than

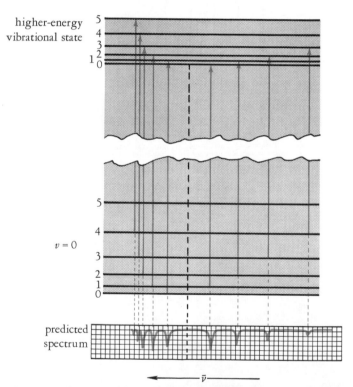

Figure 4–7 The effect of increased bond length, and decreased rotational-energy spacing, in the higher-vibrational levels exaggerated to show the relation of this factor to the asymmetry of a rotation-vibration band.

when it vibrates with the energy corresponding to $v = 0$. It follows that $I_{v=1}$ will be somewhat greater than $I_{v=0}$. Furthermore, $h^2/8\pi^2 I_{v=1}$ will be somewhat less than $h^2/8\pi^2 I_{v=0}$, and the energy spacings of the rotational levels of the $v = 1$ state will therefore be somewhat less than the spacings of the levels of the $v = 0$ state. As the greatly exaggerated diagram of Fig. 4–7 shows, this introduces the observed asymmetry into the rotation-vibration band. The $\Delta J = +1$ components, which appear on the left side of the band center, have successively an extra amount of $v = 1$ rotational energy, actually an extra amount $(2)h^2/8\pi^2 I_{v=1}$; and since this quantity is relatively small, the band components do not move out to the left as fast as one might have expected. Likewise, the $\Delta J = -1$ components, which correspond to lower energy than the band center and are on the right side of the diagram, have successively less rotational energy by the amount $(2)h^2/8\pi^2 I_{v=0}$. Since this is a relatively large amount, the components rapidly move away from the band-center position.

One can, in fact, deduce the moments of inertia for the two vibrational states involved in the vibration-rotation absorption band. The dependence of I on the amount of vibrational energy is more emphatically shown if we consider an overtone band. A suitable illustration is provided by the $v = 0$ to $v = 4$ transition of CO studied by G. Herzberg and K. N. Rao. (This is, of course, not allowed by the $\Delta v = \pm 1$ rule. However, it does occur weakly and was observed in a multiple-reflection cell with an effective path length of 2 miles at 1 atm pressure.) The rotational energies of the two vibrational states form, as shown in Fig. 4–8, the same type of pattern as was drawn for the $v = 0$ and $v = 1$ levels. Now, however, we carefully indicate the rotational spacings as being related to $I_{v=4}$ in the upper state and $I_{v=0}$ in the lower state.

Now notice, for example, the two heavy-line arrows in Fig. 4–8a. Their lengths differ by an amount that depends on the spacing in the upper $v = 4$ state. The difference in their lengths, in fact, corresponds to an energy difference of $(6)h^2/8\pi^2 I_{v=4}$. The absorptions corresponding to the two arrows are easily located, as indicated, on the observed spectrum by counting over from the band center. In this way the reported frequencies of 8421.728 and 8410.613 cm^{-1} for these two components can be used to obtain

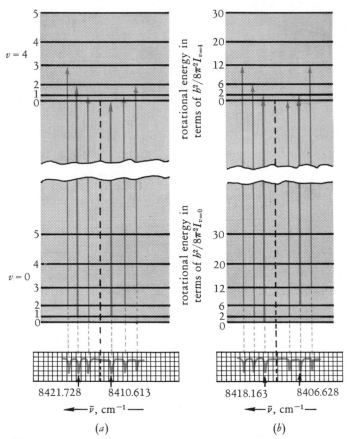

Figure 4–8   The deduction of $I_{v=0}$ and $I_{v=4}$ from the $v = 0$ to $v = 4$ rotation-vibration band components.

$$\frac{(6)h^2}{8\pi^2 I_{v=4}} = (8421.728 - 8410.613)(3 \times 10^{10})(6.627 \times 10^{-27})$$

$$= (11.115)(3 \times 10^{10})(6.627 \times 10^{-27})$$

and

$$I_{v=4} = 1.5102 \times 10^{-39} \text{ g-cm}^2.$$

Other pairs of transitions that originate at the same rotational level of the $v = 0$ vibrational state can, of course, also be used to deduce values for the moment of inertia in the $v = 4$ state. In actual practice one would obtain values of $I_{v=4}$ from various pairs of spectral lines and average the results to make full use of the information in the spectrum.

In a similar manner the moment of inertia in the ground, $v = 0$, vibrational state can be deduced. It is only necessary to find pairs of transition arrows that end at the same rotational level of the $v = 4$ state. The difference in the frequency of the absorptions to which they correspond can then be used to deduce $I_{v=0}$. The two heavy arrows of Fig. 4–8b, for example, correspond to transitions with an energy difference that can be identified with $(6)h^2/8\pi^2 I_{v=0}$. When use is made of the frequencies reported for the indicated absorption lines, one calculates

$$\frac{(6)h^2}{8\pi^2 I_{v=0}} = (8418.163 - 8406.628)(3 \times 10^{10})(6.627 \times 10^{-27})$$

$$= 12.535 \ (3 \times 10^{10})(6.627 \times 10^{-27})$$

and

$$I_{v=0} = 1.4553 \times 10^{-39} \text{ g-cm}^2.$$

Finally, with $\mu = 1.1383 \times 10^{-23}$ g one obtains

$$r_{v=4} = 1.152 \text{ A}$$

and

$$r_{v=0} = 1.131 \text{ A}$$

From this analysis we have pried further into the behavior of the molecule and have learned not only the bond length of the molecule but also the way in which the bond length depends on the extent to which the molecule is vibrating.

It can be mentioned that the fact that the bond length of a molecule depends on how much the molecule is vibrating raises some question as to what is meant by bond length. For some purposes it is adequate to use the value deduced for the lowest, $v = 0$, state. Such values, often denoted by r_0, are obtained not only from rotation-vibration bands but also from studies of pure rotational spectra, since at room temperature most molecules are in this ground vibrational state. On the other hand, it is sometimes worthwhile, and possible, to extrapolate from the values of the bond length that are deduced for various vibrational levels to obtain the value that the bond length would have if the molecule were in a state corresponding to the minimum of the potential-energy vs. internuclear-distance curve. This value is that which the molecule would have if quantum restriction did not prevent the molecule from having zero vibrational energy. Values of bond lengths at this lowest point in the potential curve, the equilibrium length the bond would adopt if the quantum restrictions did not forbid it, are usually designated as r_e.

It is interesting to notice that values of r_e are strictly independ-

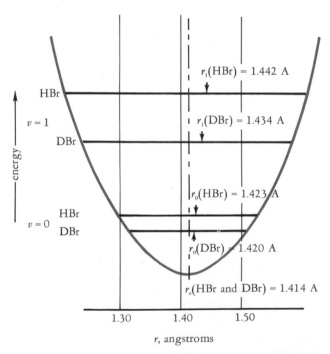

Figure 4–9   The variation of effective bond length for HBr and DBr from the minimum in the potential-energy curve, i.e., the equilibrium configuration to the first two allowed-vibrational levels.

ent of isotopic substitution, that is, r_e is the same, for example, for HBr as DBr. On the other hand, as Fig. 4–9 shows, the values of r_0 are slightly different for the two molecules. An even greater difference would, of course, show up if the effective bond lengths for higher vibrational energy states for the two molecules were tabulated. This is now readily understood, since, as shown in Fig. 4–9, the vibrational levels for DBr lie lower (the reduced mass is almost twice as great) than those for HBr, and the above discussion has shown that the value of r is dependent, to some extent, on how high in the energy scale of Fig. 4–9 the molecule is. (It is this feature that makes the use of isotopic substitution, discussed in Chap. 2, to obtain additional molecular structure data from moment-of-inertia results a little troublesome.)

The dependence of bond lengths and, for polyatomic molecules, bond angles on the amount of vibrational energy is generally a rather fine detail that need not be considered. It is introduced here to show further how molecular spectroscopy lets us look into almost every facet of a molecule's behavior.

SUMMARY

When a molecule of a gas absorbs infrared radiation, not only does the vibrational energy of the molecule change but so also may its rotational energy change. Each infrared absorption band, which is due to a particular vibrational energy change, now is found to be composed of a number of relatively closely spaced absorption lines. These components of the absorption band of gas-phase molecules can be related to the simultaneous rotational energy changes that accompany the vibrational energy change. Analysis of such vibration-rotation bands furnishes both force-constant and moment-of-inertia data and, at the same time, provides even more detailed information about the nature of the molecule.

EXERCISES

1. From data given in the preceding two chapters, plot the allowed energy levels for a CO molecule including several rotational levels in each of the $v = 0$ and $v = 1$ vibrational levels. Draw

transition arrows on this diagram and, as in Fig. 4–2, add at the bottom a schematic, predicted rotation-vibration spectrum.

2. Calculate the population of various rotational energy levels of HBr at −200°C and at +200°C, that is, 73°K and 473°K, and prepare plots for these temperatures like the plot given for 25°C in Fig. 4–6.

V

Spectra Due to Changes in the Arrangement of the Electrons of a Molecule

Quanta of radiation in the visible or ultraviolet spectral regions are sometimes absorbed, or emitted, by molecules. In such spectral transitions the electrons of the molecule acquire energy, or lose energy; and just as one talks of rotational and vibrational spectroscopy, so also one uses the term "electronic spectroscopy" for studies in the visible and ultraviolet regions. The subject can be divided into two general areas that often are experimentally different and usually provide us with different types of information on the molecules that are being studied.

The first topic that will be treated consists of the electronic spectroscopy of small molecules, and, particularly, diatomic molecules. Such studies are generally done on gas-phase samples. With such samples the absorption or emission process can lead to changes in both vibrational and rotational as well as electronic energy. Furthermore, in contrast to the experiments usually done in the spectroscopic studies discussed so far, samples at high temperatures are often studied and emission, as well as absorption, can be observed.

The second general topic deals with larger polyatomic molecules. So far, such molecules have mostly been studied in solution at room temperature, and no rotational fine structure or emission of radiation is then observed. Something about the electronic changes that occur in these larger molecules can, however, be deduced.

5-1   DIATOMIC-MOLECULAR ENERGIES FOR
DIFFERENT ELECTRONIC ARRANGEMENTS

The vast amount of information on molecules that can be obtained by spectroscopy in the microwave and infrared spectral regions usually tells us about molecules as they exist at ordinary, or room, temperature. Such molecules have whatever electronic arrangement gives them the lowest energy, i.e., makes them most stable. All molecules can, however, have other arrangements of their electrons or, as is said, other electronic states. These generally are of much higher energy than the lowest, or ground, state and are therefore not ordinarily encountered. We can, however, get information about these excited states by heating the molecules in an arc or electric discharge to thousands of degrees so that these states are populated. Then the emission of radiation by molecules in these states can be studied. One generally finds that such molecules emit ultraviolet or visible radiation when they return to the electronic arrangement of the ground state. Alternatively, one can study the high-energy electronic arrangement by shining ultraviolet or visible radiation into a sample at room temperature. From the radiation that is absorbed one can often deduce something about the high-energy state reached in the transition process.

We shall not attempt here to describe the way the electrons are arranged in the various electronic states that a molecule can have. It is enough for our purpose to state that the various possible electronic arrangements for a given molecule form a pattern of allowed electronic energies that is peculiar to the molecule and is not characterized by the uniformity and order that have characterized the vibrational and rotational energy patterns. Furthermore, since even a relatively small molecule like CO, for example, has a large number of electrons, it has so far been quite impossible to calculate the energies of various arrangements of these electrons. One must, therefore, rely on spectral measurements to provide information on the relative energies of these different electronic arrangements.

With each electronic arrangement the molecule can vibrate just as it can for the ground-state arrangement. An energy level diagram that shows the allowed vibrational energy levels for a ground state and an excited electronic state is shown in Fig. 5–1. In general, it

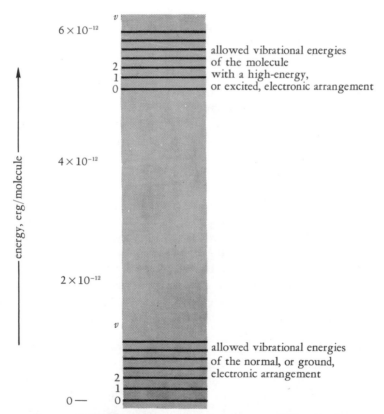

Figure 5–1 The allowed energies for two different electronic arrangements for a typical molecule. (Additional lines indicating the allowed-rotational energies are not shown.)

should be mentioned, there will be many other different electronic arrangements that the molecule could adopt. Each of these would lead to an additional set of energy levels but, for the present, it is enough to consider just one of these excited states. In addition to showing these allowed energies, it is customary to show how the potential energy of the molecule varies with internuclear distance for each electronic arrangement. This energy is nothing more than what we called potential energy when we were dealing with the molecule as a vibrating system. Then, it will be recalled, the potential energy meant the energy of the molecule exclusive of kinetic energy of vibration. We have, therefore, already had examples of the potential-energy vs. internuclear-distance curves that are drawn for given electronic states of a molecule. So far, however, these have been discussed only in terms of the ground-state electronic configurations. Potential-energy curves that belong to the allowed energy level patterns of the two states of Fig. 5–1 are included in the more generally used diagram of Fig. 5–2.

For each vibrational level of each of the two electronic states indicated in Figs. 5–1 and 5–2, a set of allowed rotational levels exist, and these might also be indicated in the diagrams. We shall see, however, that, on the scale with which these diagrams are drawn, the allowed rotational levels are so closely spaced that they could not conveniently be added to the diagram.

It usually requires visible or ultraviolet radiation to excite a molecule from its ground electronic state to a state with some higher-energy electronic arrangement. If we take 4000 A as a representative wavelength for radiation that might be absorbed in such a process, we deduce, for this radiation, a frequency of 7.5×10^{14} cycles/sec and a quantum energy of about 5×10^{-12} erg. The two sets of allowed vibrational energies shown in Figs. 5–1 and 5–2 should therefore be separated by an energy of about 5×10^{-12} erg/molecule, or 70 kcal/mole. This quantity is large compared with the energy differences that we have dealt with in rotational and vibrational effects and, furthermore, is large compared to the room temperature value of kT of 4.2×10^{-14} erg. (A typical vibrational transition, it will be recalled, occurs with the absorption of radiation with $\bar{\nu}$ values of the order of 1000 cm^{-1}. This value corresponds to $\Delta\epsilon$ values of 2×10^{-13} erg/molecule and indicates

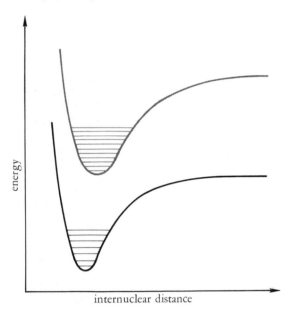

Figure 5–2   Some of the allowed energies for the two electronic arrangements of Fig. 5–1 shown with the potential-energy vs. internuclear-distance curves for the two arrangements.

that allowed vibrational energy levels are more closely spaced than different electronic states by a factor of about 10. Allowed rotational energy levels, for which a typical spacing is 10^{-16} erg/molecule, are, of course, even more closely spaced than are the vibrational spacings.)

The spacings, in Figs. 5–1 and 5–2, of the allowed vibrational energies in the two states with different electronic arrangements have been drawn in accordance with the energy quantities cited here.

5–2   ELECTRONIC TRANSITIONS—
EFFECT OF VIBRATIONAL-ENERGY CHANGES

Part of the absorption spectrum of iodine vapor will illustrate the relation between the allowed energy levels, like those of Fig. 5–2, and the spectrum obtained when the molecule absorbs or emits

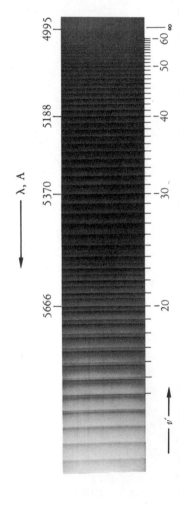

Figure 5-3 Part of the visible absorption spectrum of I₂ vapor. The numbers below the absorption lines indicate the vibrational quantum number of the molecule in the higher-energy electronic arrangement. All these transitions start from the $v = 0$ level of the ground electronic state.

radiation and goes from one electronic arrangement to another. The appropriate part of the spectrum in the visible region is shown in Fig. 5–3.

This spectrum can be obtained by passing a continuum of light, such as is emitted by a tungsten filament lamp, through a tube containing iodine vapor. This light then passes into a spectrograph so that the particular wavelengths of radiation that are absorbed can be determined. In this way one obtains the exhibited absorption spectrum. We must now see how this spectrum can be related to the energy diagram, such as the diagrams of Figs. 5–1 and 5–2, for the two electronic arrangements of I_2 that are involved in the transition.

The spectrum to be analyzed is seen immediately to consist of a very extensive series of lines that lie near 5000 A. Although the detailed structure of the absorption band will be discussed below, we begin by attributing the entire band to a change from the ground-state electronic arrangement to a higher-energy one.

Moreover, we recognize that a wavelength of 5000 A implies a frequency of about 6×10^{14} cycles/sec and a quantum energy $\Delta\epsilon$ of about 4×10^{-12} erg. Such a large quantum energy corresponds to a process involving a change in the arrangement of the electrons of the molecule.

Now let us see if we can understand some of the finer details shown by the spectrum of Fig. 5–3. We have begun by recognizing that we are now concerned principally with the change in the electronic arrangement of the molecule. However, in both the higher-energy electronic arrangement and in the lower-energy one the molecule can be vibrating and, as the energy level diagrams suggest, will have one of the allowed energies of vibration. Furthermore, the amount of vibrational energy of the molecule may well change at the same time as does the electronic energy of the molecule.

The types of transition that occur in the experiment that leads to the spectrum of Fig. 5–3 are shown in Fig. 5–4. It must be remembered that the sample is at, or near, room temperature and that the molecules are, in conformity with Boltzmann's distribution, confined principally to the $v = 0$ vibration level. It is this factor that allows the transition arrows of Fig. 5–4 to be drawn from the

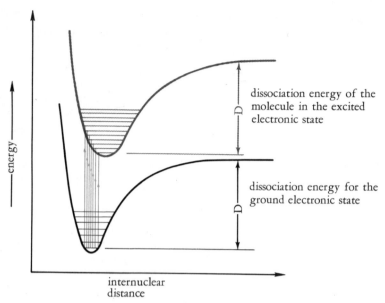

Figure 5-4   The transitions that can produce an absorption spectrum like that observed for I_2 vapor as shown in Fig. 5-3.

$v = 0$ level of the initial electronic state.   One sees, however, that the transitions end up on various vibrational levels of the upper state.   Some of the vibrational quantum numbers of the energy levels to which the transitions take the I_2 molecule are indicated beside the absorption lines due to these transitions in Fig. 5-3.

Spectra such as the spectrum of Fig. 5-3 give a wealth of information about the allowed vibrational energies for various electronic arrangements of the molecule under study.   From data on the spacings of these levels one can construct allowed vibrational energy patterns and can then work back to obtain the shape that the potential-energy curve for that electronic arrangement must have. It will be recalled, for example, that in studies of the absorption of radiation in the infrared spectral region, where the $v = 0$ to $v = 1$ transition of the ground electronic state is usually studied, it is sufficient to assume that the potential-energy curve is parabolic.

This assumption leads to a set of equispaced allowed vibrational energies as given by Eq. (18), Chap. 3, and shown in Fig. 3–4. The data contained in Fig. 5–3 show clearly, however, that if many vibrational levels are investigated, it is apparent that the spacing becomes less and less for the higher vibrational levels until finally a continuum is approached. One can see qualitatively that this implies a potential-energy curve that, like the curves of Fig. 5–2, broadens out at higher energies so that the atoms of the vibrating molecule are less closely confined and consequently the spacing between the allowed energies is smaller. More quantitative treatments can, of course, be given, and rather detailed potential-energy curves can then be drawn.

It should also be mentioned here that such studies of the vibrational energy pattern allow one to determine the energy that would be necessary to break the bond holding the atoms of the molecule together. This energy, the *dissociation energy*, is represented by D in Fig. 5–4. The dissociation energy is a quantity of considerable chemical importance, and values for this quantity are often obtained from spectroscopic measurements.

5–3 ANALYSIS OF ROTATIONAL-ENERGY CHANGES ACCOMPANYING ELECTRONIC AND VIBRATIONAL TRANSITIONS

If one now inspects each of the "lines" of a spectrum like that of Fig. 5–3 with a spectrograph that resolves the spectrum better, i.e., spreads it out along the wavelength scale so that more detail can be observed, it is found that each apparent line is itself a band of closely spaced lines. The details of such a line, or a band, as we should now call it, are shown in Fig. 5–5. This fine detail should be reminiscent of the structure of the rotation-vibration bands studied in the preceding chapter. It results, that is, from the fact that while the electronic arrangement and energy of the molecule are changing and while the vibrational energy of the molecule is changing, so also can the rotational energy change. Analysis of the rotational structure in any one of these bands is done in exactly the same way as was illustrated for a vibration-rotation band in Sec. 4–3. As in that case, one can determine the moments of inertia and the bond

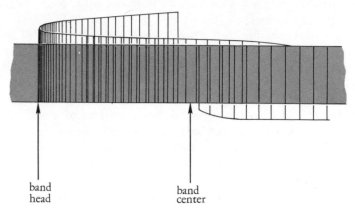

band   band
head   center

Figure 5–5 One component of an electronic band, such as that of Fig. 5–3, under high resolution. The individual lines arise because of changes in the rotational energy of the molecule that accompanies the electronic and vibrational changes that give rise to the component of the band. Note the similarity to the bands shown in Figs. 4–2, 4–3, and 4–7.

lengths in both the upper and lower energy states. Now, since the upper and lower states correspond to different electronic arrangements, one finds that these lengths can be very different. Thus for the excited electronic state of I_2 considered here the bond length is 3.02 A, while for the ground state the value is 2.67 A. This large difference is typical. As in this example, one usually finds that the electronic arrangement corresponding to the excited state does not strongly bind the nuclei together and that the bond is longer than in the ground state.

Similar analyses can sometimes be made for small, gas-phase polyatomic molecules. As in other areas of spectroscopy, the spectrum is increasingly difficult to unravel. When it can be unraveled, however, one is rewarded with a remarkable insight into the structure of the molecule in both the ground state and the excited state that is involved. For example, acetylene, H—C≡C—H, which is linear in the ground electronic state, is found to be bent in the ex-

cited state studied, and formaldehyde, $\begin{array}{c} H \\ \diagdown \\ \diagup \\ H \end{array} C\!\!=\!\!O$, which is planar in

the ground state, is found to be nonplanar, or pyramidal, in an excited state, and so forth. Such results provide new and interesting tests for our theories of chemical bonding and will lead to a better understanding of the relation between the structure and the electronic arrangement of the molecule.

5–4 ELECTRONIC SPECTRA OF LARGER MOLECULES

Let us now turn our attention to the absorption spectra of polyatomic molecules in the visible and ultraviolet regions. Such spectra are very often obtained by chemists to characterize or analyze a sample, and most often the sample is a solute in some solvent that is transparent in these regions. Just as certain absorptions in the infrared region reveal certain molecular groups, so also can visible and ultraviolet absorptions be used. This more practical application will, however, not be dealt with here. Rather, attempts will be made in the sections that follow to show what is known about the electronic changes that occur as a result of the absorption of visible and ultraviolet radiation by large molecules and how studies of these absorptions lead us to a further understanding of the electronic structures of large molecules.

It is not generally possible to locate the allowed vibrational energies and thus draw the potential-energy curves for the various electronic states of polyatomic molecules. Many vibrational degrees of freedom would exist, and the allowed-energy pattern would be correspondingly complicated. Likewise, the potential energy of a given electronic arrangement would be a function of all the bond lengths and bond angles of the molecule, and one would need a many-dimensional graph to show how the potential energy depended on all these structural parameters. One generally cannot have such a graph, and one must therefore be content with locating the energies of the various electronic arrangements simply by horizontal lines on a vertical energy scale. It follows, also, that one cannot generally do the same kind of detailed analysis of the rotational and vibrational structure of the absorption band for polyatomic molecules as one can for diatomic molecules.

For most large molecules the electronic absorption band is very complicated and one can obtain only a rather broad absorption band with little or no detail. This is particularly true when the material is studied in solution. In such cases one can only try to relate this absorption band to some electronic change in the molecule and cannot hope to deduce the actual structure of the excited electronic state. An understanding of the electronic changes that can take place is, however, of considerable interest.

The spectroscopist studying electronic spectra recognizes four different types of molecules, or groups within molecules, that are responsible for most of the electronic transitions that have been studied. In the following sections an introduction will be given to ways in which the visible or ultraviolet absorption of molecules is related to the electronic structure of the molecules, or groups within the molecule. In this way some appreciation of how the chemist makes use of electronic spectroscopy to study the electronic structure of large molecules will be obtained.

5–5   ELECTRONIC SPECTRA OF HYDROCARBONS
WITH DOUBLE BONDS

The first type of molecule that leads to visible or ultraviolet absorption that we wish to consider can be discussed in terms of compounds containing only carbon and hydrogen atoms. The student may proceed in later studies of chemistry to detailed and extensive studies of such compounds in an organic chemistry course. Although the student may already have started on studies of organic compounds, enough description of some of these molecules, and the way the electrons are arranged in them, will be given so that the basis for their absorption of radiation as a result of an electronic transition can be understood.

To begin with, we recall that the carbon atom has four outer electrons, as is represented, for example, by the Lewis diagram

$$\cdot \overset{\displaystyle \cdot}{\underset{\displaystyle \cdot}{C}} \cdot$$

Many compounds are formed when these electrons are shared between the carbon atom and four other atoms each of which also contributes an electron. The simplest hydrocarbon molecule, methane, is formed in this way from one carbon atom and four hydrogen atoms. One writes

$$
\begin{array}{c}
\text{H} \\
\text{H} \overset{\displaystyle ..}{\underset{\displaystyle ..}{:C:}} \text{H} \\
\text{H}
\end{array}
\quad \text{or} \quad
\begin{array}{c}
\text{H} \\
| \\
\text{H—C—H,} \\
| \\
\text{H}
\end{array}
$$

where the lines of the second formula represent the bonding pairs of electrons. (Our later structural formulas will be clearer if the many dots that would have to be drawn are avoided by this procedure of using a line between two atoms to represent a shared pair of electrons.)

Other hydrocarbon molecules can be built up in a way that is illustrated by the next two members of the hydrocarbon series, ethane and propane,

$$
\begin{array}{c}
\text{H \quad H} \\
| \quad | \\
\text{H—C—C—H} \\
| \quad | \\
\text{H \quad H}
\end{array}
\quad \text{and} \quad
\begin{array}{c}
\text{H \quad H \quad H} \\
| \quad | \quad | \\
\text{H—C—C—C—H} \\
| \quad | \quad | \\
\text{H \quad H \quad H}
\end{array}
$$

These molecules, in which each carbon atom is bonded by four single bonds, i.e., four separate shared pairs of electrons, to four other atoms do not absorb radiation in the visible or ultraviolet spectra regions. All the electrons of the molecule are involved in single bonds, and they cannot be rearranged to an excited state without a disruption of the molecular bonding. (This can, it should be mentioned, happen; but it requires quanta supplied by the high-energy radiation in the far-ultraviolet region, i.e., the region of shorter wavelength than that designated in Fig. 1–4 as the ultraviolet region.)

Of more interest to spectroscopists, therefore, are molecules that do not have all their electrons tied up to such an extent. It turns out that hydrocarbon molecules with double bonds, i.e., molecules in which two pairs of electrons are shared by adjacent carbon atoms, provide the electronic freedom needed. The simplest of such molecules is ethylene, which is often depicted as

$$\begin{array}{cc} \text{H}\ \ \text{H} \\ \ddot{}\ \ \ddot{} \\ \text{H:}\ddot{\text{C}}\text{::}\ddot{\text{C}}\text{:H} \qquad \text{or} \end{array} \qquad \begin{array}{c} \text{H} \qquad\qquad \text{H} \\ \diagdown \qquad\qquad \diagup \\ \text{C}=\text{C} \\ \diagup \qquad\qquad \diagdown \\ \text{H} \qquad\qquad \text{H} \end{array}$$

Spectroscopic studies have shown that ethylene is a planar molecule and that the angles made by the three groups about each carbon atom are, as suggested by the second formula, about 120°. These representations of the bonding are, however, not sufficiently detailed for our discussion of the electronic changes that occur when radiation is absorbed.

Studies of the electronic arrangement of the four electrons of the carbon atom that leads to molecules like ethylene have been made on the basis of the Schrödinger equation. One description that is based on such studies suggests that three of the electrons of each carbon atom form shared pairs with the single electrons of the three neighboring atoms in much the same way as in the completely single-bonded molecule CH_4. The quantum-mechanical studies further show that these three bonds, or shared pairs of electrons, lie in a plane and that the remaining electron of each carbon atom occupies the general region in space above and below this plane. The two electrons, one from each carbon atom, that are so arranged can also be shared, and it is this sharing that makes the bonding between the carbon atoms a double bond. This bond is known as a π bond, and the two electrons involved are said to be π electrons. The arrangement of the electrons in the ground state of ethylene can now be represented as

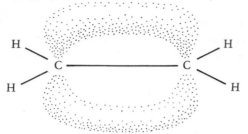

The shaded areas represent the regions in space in which the π electrons are located, and, as before, the lines represent the bonds formed by the pairs of electrons shared as in single bonds. (These latter bonds are sometimes called σ bonds to distinguish them from the π bond formed by the pair of π electrons.)

Now, unlike the situation that exists with molecules like methane and ethane, there are electrons that can be excited to a different arrangement without a complete disruption of the molecule. We find, in fact, that hydrocarbons with double bonds do absorb radiation in the visible or ultraviolet regions, and we attribute this absorption to a change involving the π electrons. Although no attempt at detailed descriptions of electronic arrangements will be made, it can be mentioned that the excited state to which ethylene goes when it absorbs ultraviolet radiation can be depicted as

This picture indicates that the two π electrons are no longer shared but rather are localized above and below each of the carbon atoms. An asterisk is usually used to indicate such a higher-energy arrangement. The above diagram therefore represents the electronic arrangement for a π^* state. Now the π bond does not exist, and the molecule has only the three single bonds to hold it together.

Of particular interest to spectroscopists are hydrocarbon molecules in which double and single bonds occur alternately between the
carbon atoms. The simplest such molecule is butadiene, which is
simply represented as

Its equilibrium configuration is also completely planar and has the
shape indicated. The more detailed diagram that can be drawn to
show something of the electronic structure is

The point of particular interest is that the π electron of, for example,
the second carbon atoms can be shared either with that of the first
carbon atom or with that of the third carbon atom. The net effect
of such different arrangements is to give an over-all π-electron distribution that might be depicted as

One says that the π electrons are "delocalized." This delocalization has spectroscopic significance when one recalls the statement of Sec. 1–3 about quantum restrictions, which is now turned around to say: the quantum restrictions are less important; i.e., the allowed energies are more closely spaced the larger the region in space in which the particles can move. We expect on this basis that the allowed energies of the π electrons of butadiene will be more closely spaced than those of ethylene. Spectroscopic results bear this out in that butadiene absorbs quanta with an energy of 9.5×10^{-12} erg ($\lambda = 2100$ A), while those absorbed by ethylene have quantum energies of about 11.4×10^{-12} erg ($\lambda = 1750$ A). These absorptions occur far out in the ultraviolet spectra region.

The delocalization effect is much more dramatic in the case of very long conjugated chains of double bonds. As the number of double bonds increases, the allowed energy levels become more closely spaced and the absorption band moves from the ultraviolet to the visible region, i.e., the region of smaller quantum energies.

By the time there are about ten double bonds, with alternating single bonds, the compounds appear colored. Thus, the compound carotene, which has eleven double bonds so arranged, contributes the characteristic color to carrots. Likewise, a compound with nine alternating double and single bonds, known as lutein, gives egg yolks their yellow color.

Much more quantitative treatments of the absorption due to π-electron excitation can be given, and perhaps they will be encountered by the student in more advanced courses. Such treatments will, however, bear out the qualitative idea of delocalization that has been introduced here.

5–6   ELECTRONIC SPECTRA DUE TO
NONBONDING ELECTRONS

In the preceding section it is pointed out that electrons can be excited to higher-energy configurations by the absorption of radiation. Now we ask: Are there any electrons in a molecule, other than the π electrons of hydrocarbon molecules, that can be relatively easily excited? One might try to think of molecules in which there are outer electrons that are not directly involved in holding together the atoms of the molecule by the single bonds of the molecule. As we shall point out, there are such electrons, known as *nonbonding* electrons, and they can be illustrated by the carbonyl group $\diagdown C = O$.

This is an important and often-encountered group in organic chemistry. The simplest compound with this group is formaldehyde, H_2CO, which can be depicted as

$$\begin{array}{c} H \\ \diagdown \\ \qquad C = \ddot{O}: \\ \diagup \\ H \end{array}$$

One finds many other carbonyl compounds, the one most often encountered probably being the common solvent acetone,

$$\begin{array}{c} O \\ \parallel \\ CH_3 - C - CH_3. \end{array}$$

Now let us consider more specifically the electronic arrangement of the carbonyl group. One first writes the Lewis diagram

$$\begin{array}{c} H \\ \cdot\cdot \quad \cdot\cdot \\ H : C : : \ddot{O} : \;. \end{array}$$

One can then proceed to a more detailed diagram by looking on formaldehyde as, in some regards, the counterpart of ethylene but with one of the CH_2 groups replaced by an oxygen atom. The parallel is extended if one recognizes that the six outer electrons of oxygen can be arranged to give the picture

where the four outer electrons of the oxygen atom that are not involved in the bonding have been indicated as occupying positions in
space like those of electron pairs of the carbon atom that are involved
in bonding to the hydrogen atoms.

In spectral studies we must now allow for the possibility that
either the π electrons, as discussed before, or the nonbonding electrons are excited to some higher energy state as a result of the absorption of radiation quanta. Experimental results indicate that
both excitations can occur. Although it is a matter of some difficulty to relate an observed visible or ultraviolet absorption band
to a particular electronic transition, it now seems established that
both the π electrons and the n, that is, nonbonding, electrons can be
excited to the π^* state as a result of the absorption of radiation. The
way in which the absorption of radiation is related to these electronic changes is illustrated in Fig. 5–6.

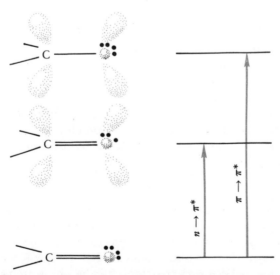

Figure 5–6 An electronic-energy-level diagram for the carbonyl group showing two of the excited states that are important in spectroscopy. In both excited states, an electron has
been promoted to a π^* orbital, indicated by the shaded areas.

Chemists are now making great strides toward accomplishing assignments such as those indicated in Fig. 5–6. The result of this work will be a deeper understanding of the energies of various electronic arrangements of molecules. This better understanding is certain to play an important role in attempts to understand chemical reactions, i.e., the way in which molecules come together and adopt an electronic and nuclear configuration different from that of the free ground-state molecules and finally rearrange to give new product molecules.

Now let us turn from these examples from organic chemistry to an area of electronic spectroscopy that is closely tied to the developing theories of an area of inorganic chemistry.

5–7   ELECTRONIC SPECTRA
OF METAL IONS

The absorption of light by molecules of the types discussed in the preceding sections is familiar to everyone in that the colors of, for example, carrots and tomatoes are due to the presence of such molecules. When the student begins the study of chemistry, he will encounter many more colored compounds. Perhaps the most remarkable display of colors, which of course correspond to absorptions of radiation in the visible spectral region, is noticed when the ions of transition metals and the reactions of these metal ions are studied. The student might, for instance, have occasion to add ammonium hydroxide to a solution of cupric chloride, $CuCl_2$. When this is done, the solution changes from a light green to a very intense blue. The blue color is attributed to the ion

$$Cu(NH_3)_4{}^{2+},$$

in which four NH_3 molecules are attached, or *coordinated*, to the Cu^{2+} ion. Many metal ions form such coordinated ions, sometimes with two, most often with six, coordinating groups rather than four. Many of these ions are colored. Let us now see what electronic change is occurring that leads to the absorption of visible radiation and hence the observed colors.

In the preceding two sections we dealt with the electrons of first-row elements such as C and O. The electrons of these elements, as will be recalled from studies of atomic structure and the periodic table, are characterized by a quantum number l that has the value of 0 or 1. The electrons are known as s and p electrons. When one deals with elements farther along the periodic table, one encounters elements for which $l = 2$. Electrons that occupy orbitals for which $l = 2$ are known as d electrons. It will be recalled, moreover, that when the quantum number l has the value 2, the magnetic quantum number m can have the values 2, 1, 0, -1, -2. There are, therefore, five different d orbitals each corresponding to a different value of m and, therefore, to a different orientation in space. Each of these orbitals can accommodate two electrons, since one electron can have its spin pointing in one direction and the other have its spin oppositely directed. (The student will recall that when the relation between atomic structure and the periodic table was studied, the Pauli exclusion principle, that no two electrons of an atom could have all quantum numbers the same, was used. Now we see that if two electrons occupy a given d orbital, they must have different electron spin quantum numbers, that is, $+\frac{1}{2}$ and $-\frac{1}{2}$.)

Most of the metals that lead to colored ions are those known as the transition metals. The student may already know that the ions of these metals have some d electrons, but not the full complement of 10 d electrons that would fill, pairwise, the available five d orbitals.

Now let us see if we can understand why, when transition-metal ions (i.e., those with incomplete sets of d electrons) coordinate with groups such as the NH_3 group, visible light may be absorbed and the solution may be colored.

The basis for the tendency of coordination compounds of the transition metals to be colored can be seen if we first draw pictures to show how the d electrons of the ion must arrange themselves in space and then draw in the groups that coordinate to the ion to form the often-colored species.

Just as pictures can be drawn for the s and p orbitals to show how electrons in these orbits are arranged in space, so also can one do this for d orbitals. The five pictures that are drawn are shown in Fig. 5–7.

One should note, since it will be an important feature, that two

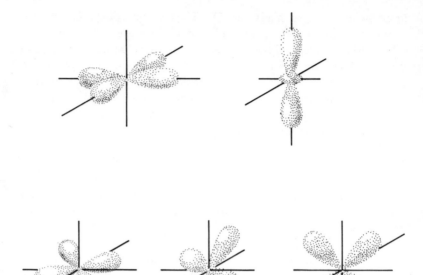

Figure 5–7   The angular factors describing the distribution in space of an electron in a *d* orbit.

of the orbitals point along the coordinate axes, whereas the other three have the four directions in which they would concentrate an electron directed in between the coordinate axes.

When an ion is in the gas phase, the directions in which the *d* orbitals point is of no consequence. An electron in any of the *d* orbits would have the same energy. In fact, one would draw the rather trivial set of five lines at the left of Fig. 5–8 to show that, for a gas-phase ion, there are five *d* orbitals. The diagram implies that, if a metal ion has a number of *d* electrons, these electrons will all have the same energy. (Here we ignore the complicating fact that the electrons will repel each other because of their negative charge.) The electrons will, furthermore, be distributed in space according to whichever of the diagrams of Fig. 5–7 represents the orbital occupied. It might be mentioned, however, that because the electrons

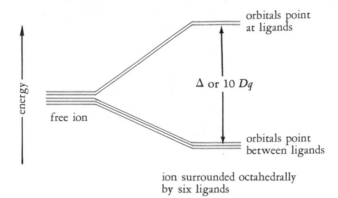

Figure 5–8 The relative effect, on the energy of an electron, of the electrostatic repulsion between the coordinating ligands and the electron in the various d orbitals.

repel one another, they tend to avoid pairing up in the same orbit. Thus if an ion has five d electrons, as Mn^{2+} has, each electron will occupy one of the energy levels of Fig. 5–8 and each will be arranged in space according to one of the five pictures of Fig. 5–7.

Now let us see what happens when the ion is not a free gas-phase ion but rather is surrounded by a number of coordinating groups. Let us restrict our attention to cases in which there are six coordinating groups, or *ligands*, as they are called, and these are arranged symmetrically about the central ion as shown for the example, $Ni(NH_3)_6^{2+}$, in Fig. 5–9. The NH_3 groups are attracted to the Ni^{2+} ion because the NH_3 molecule has a negative end and a projecting pair of electrons, as is emphasized by representing the ammonia molecule as

$$:NH_3 \quad \text{or} \quad \begin{array}{c} \vdots \end{array} \quad N \begin{array}{c} \diagup H \\ \!\!\!\!-H, \\ \diagdown H \end{array}$$

where the second diagram attempts to show the geometry of the ammonia molecule. Now, how does the presence of six groups, each

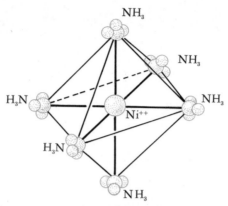

Figure 5–9 The complex [Ni(NH₃)₆]²⁺ showing the octahedral arrangement of the six NH₃ ligands.

with a pair of projecting electrons, affect the d orbitals of the metal ion?

Clearly, the electrons of the metal ion are going to be repelled by the electrons of the ligands, and as a result the metal electrons will tend to be located in d orbitals that allow them to avoid, as much as possible, the attached ligands. If one looks again at Fig. 5–7 and now imagines the ligand groups with their projecting electrons to be located at the ends of the coordinate axes, one sees that three of the d orbitals will keep the metal-ion electrons away from the ligands, while two of the orbitals will point the metal-ion electrons directly at the ligands. It follows that now the five d orbitals will not all give electrons the same energy. The effect can be represented by showing the energies for the set of d orbitals split into two sets as shown on the right of Fig. 5–8. The three d orbitals that keep the metal-ion electrons away from the ligands provide the three low-lying energy levels, while the two d orbitals that point at the ligands lead to the two high energy levels.

The ligands produce an effect because of their particular arrangement about the metal ion and because the electric field that their electrons produce acts to change the energies of some d orbitals relative to other *d* orbitals. Because of these two features the separation of the sets of levels is known as the *crystal field splitting* or the *ligand field splitting*. Furthermore, the separation of the two sets of levels that result from the effect of six ligands octahedrally placed is, as shown in Fig. 5–8, referred to as Δ or, alternatively, as 10 *Dq*. The student may encounter either symbol and should recognize that the value of this parameter, Δ or 10 *Dq*, gives a measure of the magnitude of the interaction between the ligands and the *d* electrons of the metal ion.

Now the basis for an electronic transition that absorbs visible radiation has been presented. A *d* electron in the low-energy level can pick up a quantum of radiation and move to the high-energy set of levels. The absorption of radiation is seen now to depend on the presence of some *d* electrons, i.e., at least one and less than the complete complement of ten, in the metal ion and the existence of electron-repelling groups, i.e., ligands, located in certain positions around the ion. The ions of the coordination compounds of transition metals fulfill these two requirements, and we now understand, therefore, the tendency of these ions to be colored. (By contrast, metal ions such as Ca^{2+} and Zn^{2+}, which have, respectively, none and ten *d* electrons, tend not to give colored solutions, as the student has undoubtedly noticed.)

Just as observation of absorption bands of all types has allowed

energy

Figure 5–10 The transition of one *d* electron of a metal ion surrounded by six ligands in octahedral positions. (An example is $[Ti(H_2O)_6]^{3+}$, for which the transition gives rise to an absorption band at 4900 A, or 20,400 cm^{-1}.)

us to deduce the spacing between allowed energy levels, so also can the position of the absorption band, or bands, of a transition metal ion be used to deduce the spacing of the sets of energy levels, like those of Fig. 5–8, that result from the presence of the ligands.

The simplest situation, if not the chemically most familiar one, is that when there is just one d electron. Then the repulsions that occur between d electrons do not enter to complicate the analysis and the value of Δ, or 10 Dq, can be obtained directly from the position of the absorption band. The transition arrow of Fig. 5–10 shows the transition that occurs, and it is clear that the energy of the quanta absorbed is equal to the crystal field splitting parameter. It is customary to report values of Δ, or 10 Dq, in the often-used spectroscopic energy units of centimeters^{-1}. In these units the splittings observed are of the order of 20,000 cm^{-1}, and it follows that absorption in the visible region is to be expected. This is illustrated in Fig. 5–11 by the spectrum due to the ion $[\mathrm{Ti(H_2O)_6}]^{3+}$. The relation between the visible spectrum and the d-orbital splitting, illus-

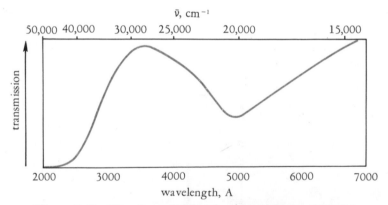

Figure 5–11 The absorption band, with maximum at 4900 A or 20,400 cm^{-1}, found in the spectrum of an aqueous solution of Ti$_2$(SO$_4$)$_3$ and attributable to the octahedral ion $[\mathrm{Ti(H_2O)_6}]^{3+}$. Recall that the visible region extends from about 4000 to 8000 A. (The absorption in the ultraviolet is probably due to a charge-transfer process.) [Adapted from the spectrum of E. Ilse and H. Hartmann, *Z. Physik. Chem.*, **197**, 239 (1951).]

trated here for the simple one-d-electron situation suggests how the relative extent of interaction of different ligand groups, as characterized by Δ, or 10 Dq, could be evaluated from the absorption spectra of transition-metal ions in the visible region.

The many interesting aspects that studies of the spectra of solutions of metal ions raise cannot be dealt with here. Ligands often adopt different arrangements about a metal ion than that used here to illustrate the principal features. Furthermore, different numbers of ligands occur about various transition metals. The ligands themselves can be of quite different types, i.e., they could be Cl^-, F^-, H_2O, and so forth. The treatment introduced here can, however, be extended to many of these situations so that one can often understand—in terms of the nature of the metal ion, its number of d electrons, and the electron-repelling effect of the coordinating groups—why various solutions of metal ions have various colors.

5-8 CHARGE-TRANSFER SPECTRA

The fourth and final basic type of electronic rearrangement that results from the absorption of quanta of radiation will now be introduced. A simple laboratory experiment, or lecture demonstration, can illustrate that the absorption of radiation can depend on an electron of one molecule picking up energy and, instead of going to some higher energy level of the same molecule, going to a high energy level of a neighboring molecule. A solution of I_2 in an inert solvent, perhaps carbon tetrachloride or a hydrocarbon, gives the same violet color as does iodine vapor. The color is therefore due to the absorption of light by individual I_2 molecules. If now, any one of a number of molecular types, perhaps benzene, pyridine, alcohol, or ether, is added, the solution turns a deep brown color. No appreciable reaction occurs between the I_2 and the added molecules. They may come together and be loosely held neighbors. The dramatic spectral changes that occur must be attributed to some process involving both the I_2 molecule and the added molecule. It appears that the electron of one molecule absorbs a quantum of the visible radiation and is excited, not to a higher energy level of this molecule but rather to one of the vacant high energy levels of the neighboring molecule. Such a process is known as *charge-transfer absorption*.

It now appears that such charge-transfer processes are not at all unusual. Generally, however, quanta of rather high energy are necessary to perform the processes, and the absorption bands due to the process are then found in the ultraviolet region. The energy needed to transfer the electron is related primarily to the ionization potential of the molecule from which the electron is removed, but the electron affinity of the molecule receiving the electron may also have an effect.

For systems involving I_2 and basic, or electron-rich, molecules the absorption band that is attributable to the charge-transfer process is found as illustrated in Fig. 5–12, at about 2900 A. The exact position of the band, however, is related to the ionization potential of the basic molecule. The lower the ionization potential, the lower the quantum energies and the longer the wavelength of radiation absorbed. One concludes, therefore, that in these systems the charge-transfer process involves the transfer of an electron from a

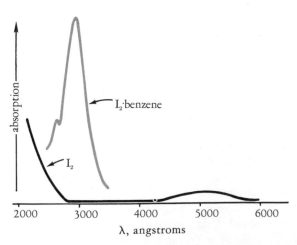

Figure 5–12 The absorption band, due to charge transfer, of the complex $I_2 \cdot$benzene. For comparison, the absorption of I_2 dissolved in a noninteracting solvent such as CCl_4 is also shown. Benzene does not absorb appreciably in the region shown.

neighboring base molecule to one of the high-energy empty orbitals of the I_2 molecule. Intramolecular processes very comparable to these intermolecular electron transfers are also recognized. Perhaps the simplest example is provided by the absorption of ultraviolet radiation, at a wavelength of about 2340 A, by gas-phase NaCl molecules. The ground electronic state of these molecules is rather well represented by a completely ionic structure, as represented by Na^+Cl^-. The observed ultraviolet absorption band is attributed to the absorption of quanta that have the effect of transferring one of the electrons from the Cl^- ion in the Na^+Cl^- molecule to one of the available orbitals located primarily on the Na^+ ion. The excited state is, therefore, in effect a covalently bound NaCl molecule, and the electron transfer absorption process can be represented as

$$Na^+Cl^- \xrightarrow{h\nu} Na\text{—}Cl.$$

Many similar intramolecular electron transfer processes are now recognized in the spectra of complex ions in solution. For example, the ion $[Co(NH_3)_5Cl]^{2+}$, in addition to showing the absorption bands due to d-electron transitions on the Co^{3+} ion that were discussed in Sec. 5–7, gives a very intense absorption in the ultraviolet region at 2275 A. Again the electronic change that accompanies this absorption can be attributed to the transfer of an electron from the Cl^- ion to the metal ion as is represented by the reaction

It should be noticed that electron transfer processes, such as those mentioned here, lead to the movement of electrons between groups that are not necessarily covalently bonded. Since the move-

ment of electrons through chemical systems is an important phenomenon in many situations—in biological systems, for example—
studies of the electron transfers that result from the absorption of
radiation give promise of helping to elucidate many phenomena that
are as yet little understood.

SUMMARY

The rather high energy quanta that occur in the visible and
ultraviolet regions are absorbed by some molecules and ions, and, as
a consequence, the energy of the electrons of the molecule or ion is
increased.

For a number of types of molecules the electronic change that accompanies the absorption of visible or ultraviolet radiation can be
described. The frequency of the observed absorption band then
gives information on the relative energies of the normally encountered and the excited electronic arrangements.

If the sample is in the form of a gas, the rotational and vibrational energy of the molecule will generally change during the
absorption process. Analysis of the structure of the electronic absorption band .then provides information on the rotational and
vibrational energies, and therefore on the size, shape, and flexibility,
of the molecule with both its normal and its higher-energy electronic
arrangement.

Although considerable information on the structures of diatomic
molecules with various electronic arrangements has been obtained
from the electronic spectra of gas-phase systems, only a start has been
made on extending such studies to polyatomic molecules. Moments
of inertia and force constants of some such molecules are already
known for the electronic arrangements adopted by these molecules
at room temperature from studies of their rotational and vibrational spectra. Similar information, which will make a great impact
on our ideas about chemical bonding and on our concepts about the
excited states adopted by molecules in the course of chemical reactions, has yet to be obtained for many molecules of general chemical
interest. Studies in this area, the electronic spectroscopy of gas-
phase molecules, will lead to an important extension of our knowledge of the geometry of excited states of molecules.

Much similar work remains to be done to provide the chemist with an adequate understanding of the arrangement of the electrons in excited states of polyatomic molecules. Such studies also represent, therefore, a general area in which much progress is to be expected. The greatest potential, perhaps, lies in the phenomenon of electron transfer processes. It seems likely that studies of the ground and excited electronic states that are connected by an absorption or emission of radiation and involve a transfer of an electron will lead to important new concepts regarding the location and movement of electrons in chemical systems.

EXERCISES

1. Some of the spectral lines attributable to transitions from the $v = 0$ level of the ground state and various values of v of the upper state are labeled and their wavelengths can be read off in Fig. 5–3. Calculate the frequency and quantum energies of a series of these lines. Make a vibrational energy level diagram to scale for this series and notice the convergence of the allowed energies.

2. From the results of the preceding exercise extrapolate, as best you can, to the spacing of the $v = 0$ and $v = 1$ levels of the upper electronic state and calculate the force constant for the I_2 molecule in that electronic state. Compare with the force constant of 1.7×10^5 dynes/cm for I_2 in the ground-state electronic arrangement. (One finds generally that the higher-energy electronic arrangements lead to a looser or more flexible bond.)

VI

The Emission or Dissipation of Energy by Excited Molecules

In the preceding chapters attention has been paid to the absorption of electromagnetic radiation energy by molecules. In the processes considered the molecule goes, as a result of this energy-absorption process, to a rotational, vibrational, or electronic state that corresponds to a higher energy than that of the molecule originally. In most studies of the absorption spectrum of molecules the amount of radiation absorbed by a given transition, for example, from the $v = 0$ to the $v = 1$ level of some vibrational mode of a molecule, does not decrease if the radiation that brings about the transition is continually passed through the sample. This observation is understandable if the molecules that have absorbed radiation return to their initial state very soon after the excitation process. If they do so, the population of the initial state will not be significantly reduced by the absorption of radiation. We conclude, therefore, that in some systems at least, the molecules that are raised to a higher energy state must have some relatively effective way, or ways, of losing the excess energy so that they return to the initial state.

It is appropriate in this closing chapter to investigate the ways in which molecules can get rid of the excess energy that they have acquired as a result of the absorption of radiation. Two principal mechanisms can be recognized, and they will be dealt with separately. The first of these depends on the transfer of energy between molecules that collide, or at least are nearby; and in this situation the energy need not be radiated away from the excited molecule. Such processes are described as *nonradiative* ones. The second general mechanism for energy dissipation involves the emission of electromagnetic radiation from the excited molecule. Various types of *radiative* processes will be identified and discussed.

6-1 NONRADIATIVE ENERGY-TRANSFER PROCESSES

An understanding of the ways in which molecules can come together and exchange energy is important for the study of a number of chemical phenomena. For example, if a gas or liquid is suddenly compressed, and thereby heated, it is of interest to know how rapidly the various types of energy levels available to the molecules become populated in accordance with the Boltzmann distribution for the new temperature. We shall not attempt here to approach such general problems, and it will be enough for our purpose to provide a background against which the more spectroscopically interesting phenomenon of radiative energy dissipation can be understood.

An initial understanding of how long an excited gas molecule might retain its excess energy before it passes this energy, or part of it, on to another molecule of the gas can be reached by calculating the average time that a gas molecule has between collisions with other molecules. This quantity, or often the inverse of it, i.e., the number of collisions that a gas molecule makes per second, is obtained from the kinetic-molecular theory of gas behavior. It will be sufficient here to mention the pertinent results. For relatively small molecules one calculates that, at 1-atm pressure, a molecule suffers a collision about every 10^{-10} sec. This length of time between collisions increases, as would be expected, as the pressure is reduced; and furthermore, in the region of very low pressures, collisions with the walls of the container also become important and affect the calculation.

In the liquid state the concept of molecular collisions is less straightforward. It has been estimated, however, that a molecule in a liquid collides with a neighboring molecule about 10^{13} times per sec. This leads to a time between collisions of about 10^{-13} sec, and this value, in view of the greater proximity of the molecules in a liquid than in a gas at 1 atm, seems reasonable.

These values, 10^{-10} and 10^{-13} sec, give an idea of the shortest times in which the transfer of energy from an average excited molecule could occur. In fact, there is no reason to expect that all collisions will be effective in transferring energy; and, moreover, it should not be expected that rotational, vibrational, and electronic energies should be equally transferable.

It is a matter of some difficulty, and current research interest, to determine the probability that a collision will result in the transfer of a given excess molecular energy. Some qualitative ideas have, however, been developed.

It appears, for example, that rotational energy is relatively easily transferred and that most collisions are in fact effective in the exchange of such energy. Frequencies associated with typical molecular rotations are, as can be checked from the data in Chap. 2, of the order of 10^{11} or 10^{12} cycles, or rotations, per second. Alternatively, we say that it takes about 10^{-11} or 10^{-12} sec for one rotation of a molecule. We see, therefore, that in gases at pressures lower than 1 atm many rotations occur between collisions, and deactivation, but that in liquids the molecules generally will not be able to complete a rotation in the short time of about 10^{-13} sec that exists on the average between collisions. We conclude, therefore, that in liquids the molecules are not free to rotate, and this conclusion is consistent with our observations that vibrational absorption bands generally show rotational fine structure only when the sample is a gas.

On the other hand, vibrational energy is less readily exchanged. The importance of the type of vibration that is excited is not yet clear, but it appears that something like 10^4 collisions might be required, on the average, before one that brings about the transfer of vibrational energy will occur. In such a "transfer" the excess vibrational energy probably appears as additional rotational and translational energy of both the colliding molecules. A vibrationally excited molecule in the liquid state may, therefore, have a lifetime of the order of $10^4 \times 10^{-13} = 10^{-9}$ sec. This time is, it should be noted, long compared with the period of about 10^{-13} sec for a typical vibration. A molecule, even in a liquid, will therefore complete many vibrational cycles before it is deactivated.

Finally, let us consider the way in which a molecule whose electronic arrangement and energy have been affected by the absorption of visible or ultraviolet light can dissipate the excess energy and return to its normal, or ground, electronic state. This process is relatively difficult; and to investigate it further, one needs to consider a number of different situations.

The simplest situation is that illustrated for an excited state and the ground electronic state in Fig. 6–1. The allowed vibrational energies for each electronic arrangement are shown. In addition, the potential-energy vs. internuclear-distance curves that can be deduced from each set of vibrational levels and, therefore, that correspond to each electronic arrangement, are shown. The absorption of radia-

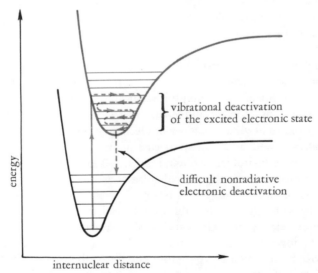

Figure 6–1 The absorption and nonradiative deactivation for electronic states corresponding to the potential-energy curves shown. The dashed arrow is intended to suggest that collisions generally remove the excess vibrational energy one step at a time.

tion that produces the higher-energy electronic configuration can be represented, as discussed in the preceding chapter, by the vertical arrow. We must generally ask, therefore, how the molecule in a high-energy vibrational state and a high-energy electronic arrangement loses all this excess energy.

The excess vibrational energy can be lost, as mentioned above, by repeated collisions with neighboring molecules; and in the liquid state, in the course of about 10^{-9} sec, the process schematically indicated by the dashed line will be complete. Further dissipation of energy would require, for the situation represented in Fig. 6–1, the removal of a large amount of energy in a single collision and the simultaneous rearrangement of the electronic structure of the molecule so that the ground-state electronic configuration would be reached. It must be expected that it will be very unlikely for such a complicated process to accompany a single molecular collision. It appears that such electronic deactivation by a collision process is very improbable. The dissipation of energy from the lowest vibrational level of an excited electronic state such as that of Fig. 6–1 usually occurs as a result of emission of energy as radiation, i.e., will generally be accomplished by a radiative process. Such processes will be treated in more detail in the following section.

For most molecules, however, the representation of Fig. 6–1 must be recognized as a simplification that is not valid. In the energy region not too far above that of the ground electronic state there will normally be a number of electronic arrangements. These arrangements will have potential-energy curves that will cross one another, and the situation shown in Fig. 6–2 must be expected to be more representative of the typical state of affairs. With such a diagram it is possible, as suggested by the dashed line, for all the excess energy to be lost by small, vibrational-sized steps. It appears that the deactivation path that is followed takes the originally excited molecule down through the vibrational levels of the initial excited state to a level where the potential energy of the first excited state crosses that of another state. At this crossing point both electronic arrangements have, at a particular molecular geometry, the same potential energy. At such a point it may be relatively easy for the electronic arrangement to change from that corresponding to one set of allowed energy levels and the corresponding potential curve to

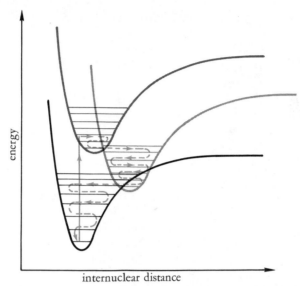

internuclear distance

Figure 6-2 The absorption and nonradiative deactivation of an excited electronic state where the potential-energy curves for various electronic arrangements allow, by means of internal conversion, the original ground state to be reached after a series of vibrational-energy steps.

that corresponding to the other set of levels and the other potential curve. This process, known as *internal conversion*, appears to be much more probable than is the change in electronic arrangement that must be accompanied by a large energy transfer. It is by the processes of vibrational deactivation and internal conversion that a molecule raised to an excited state such as that of Fig. 6-2 can return to its initial ground electronic and vibrational state by nonradiative processes.

It should be mentioned, in connection with a situation that will be very important when radiative processes are considered, that even when potential-energy curves for two different electronic arrangements cross, it is not necessarily an easy matter for the electronic arrangement to change over from the arrangement that corresponds to one of the potential-energy curves to the arrangement that corresponds to the other curve. This difficulty is most noticeable when the two electronic arrangements are such that the number of unpaired electrons is different in the two arrangements. Most often, one deals with situations in which one arrangement has no unpaired electrons and the other arrangement has one pair of electrons broken up so that there are two unpaired electrons. The former arrangement constitutes what is labeled a *singlet state*, while the latter is known as a *triplet state*. It appears that internal conversion between singlet and triplet states can occur but that it is not as rapid and easy a process as conversion between electronic arrangements with equal numbers of unpaired electrons. The mechanism by which the direction of the spin of one electron relative to another is changed is apparently not very effective. Nevertheless, crossing over from one potential curve to another, with different net spin, can occur and nonradiative processes can, even in this case, return the molecule to its initial state.

The transfer of energy in a collision is, as would be expected, more probable the harder the two molecules collide with each other, i.e., the more they interact during the collision. This interaction can be greatly decreased, and the nonradiative energy transfers greatly impeded, by two effects. The first consists of cooling the sample down to liquid-nitrogen or liquid-helium temperatures and thereby decreasing the kinetic energy of the molecules and the effectiveness of collisions. In the second place the number of collisions can be decreased by dissolving the molecules under study in a solvent which, when cooled, sets to a rigid glassy material. (If the solvent crystallizes, it will generally form pure crystals and leave the material in solution to form separate crystals.) Often used for the formation of a glass is a mixture of ether, isopentane, and ethanol, although many other suitable materials that set to glasses rather than form crystals are known. When materials are embedded in such glasses and cooled to low temperatures, the nonradiative processes for the elimination of the excess energy absorbed by a molecule are very ineffective and then the radiative processes become important.

6–2   FLUORESCENT EMISSION OF RADIATION

Let us now return to a situation corresponding to the simple system represented in Fig. 6–1. We might furthermore, although for many systems this would not be necessary, consider the sample to be cooled to low temperatures in a glassy solvent. The nonradiative collision processes will again bring the excited molecule down to the lowest vibrational level of the electronically excited state. At this point, especially for cooled rigid systems, no further collision-type processes will occur.

Now that the competing nonradiative processes have been eliminated, one finds that the molecule can *spontaneously emit* radiation. Typically, half the molecules in the excited electronic arrangement will emit their excess energy spontaneously in about 10^{-8} sec. This process therefore must normally compete with nonradiative processes, and only in rather special cases is it observed.

When such spontaneous emission is observed, one finds, as the two vertical arrows of Fig. 6–3 suggest, that the quanta of the emitted radiation have less energy than those of the absorbed radia-

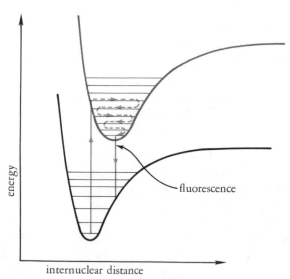

Figure 6–3 Emission of radiation as fluorescence, showing that vibrational deactivation of the excited state leads to fluorescent radiation that will be of lower energy, or longer wavelength, than the absorbed radiation.

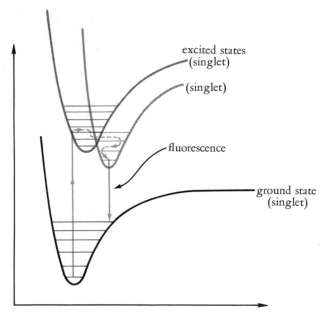

Figure 6–4 Fluorescence following internal conversion. Most molecules have no unpaired electrons in their ground-electronic state; for internal conversion and fluorescent emission to readily occur, as indicated here, both the exhibited excited electronic states must also have no unpaired electrons; i.e., they must also be singlet states.

tion. This leads to the occurrence of the emission band at lower frequencies, or longer wavelength, than the corresponding absorption band. A similar situation results if emission occurs from one of the excited electronic states reached by internal conversion. The process then would be that shown in Fig. 6–4. The experimental observations, such as those shown in Fig. 6–5, bear out the expectations regarding the relative absorption and emission wavelengths.

Emission of radiation, it should be mentioned, is still possible even with the electronic arrangements like those that lead to the potential-energy curves shown in Fig. 6–2. It is only necessary in

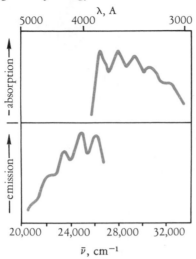

Figure 6–5 The absorption and fluorescence of anthracene, showing that the fluorescent band occurs at longer wavelengths than the absorption band.

such a situation to have the return to the ground state by nonradiative processes sufficiently slow that the radiative process can compete.

As for nonradiative processes it turns out that the radiative process is greatly affected by the numbers of unpaired electrons in the two states involved in the emission process. Although no specific statement has been made, we have been assuming so far that the emission process connects two states with the same number of unpaired electrons—two singlet states or two triplet states, for example. Such emission is known as *fluorescent emission*, or *fluorescence*, and it is such emission that occurs typically with the relatively short half-lives. Experimentally one finds half-lives for fluorescence in the range 10^{-9} to about 10^{-4} sec. It is clear that the decay of fluorescence following a turning off of the exciting radiation is so rapid that it can be observed and studied only with very fast electronic equipment.

In addition to this rapid emission process, there is a slow, more easily observed one that will be discussed now.

6-3 · PHOSPHORESCENT EMISSION
OF RADIATION

Phosphorescent emission, or *phosphorescence*, is the name applied to the spontaneous emission of radiation when the initial and final states involved in the process have different numbers of unpaired electrons.   Again the pairing or unpairing of electrons is a difficult process, and when this is a requirement for the radiation process to occur, the process tends to be a rather slow one.   The half-lives for phosphorescence, i.e., the times, after the exciting beam is shut off, for the phosphorescent radiation to decrease to half its intensity, are found generally to be in the range from about 10^{-3} sec up to a number of minutes.   The slowing down of the emission process that accom-

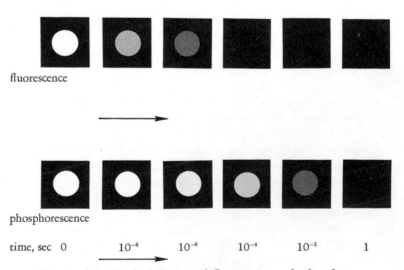

Figure 6-6 Typical decays of fluorescent and phosphorescent emission following the shutting off of the light that excites the sample.

panies a change in the number of unpaired electrons is shown graphically in Fig. 6–6.

Just as it is difficult for molecules to emit radiation if in the process the number of unpaired electrons must change, so also is it difficult for molecules to absorb radiation if a net electron spin change must occur. The question that then arises is how excited-state molecules that have a different number of unpaired electrons than do the ground-state molecules can be obtained. Almost all molecules in their ground state have all their electrons paired, i.e., are in singlet states with no unpaired electrons. Any reasonably intense absorption band of such singlet-state molecules will correspond to a process, such as that indicated by the arrow of Fig. 6–7, in which an excited singlet state is achieved. (Absorptions leading to triplet excited states can sometimes be detected, but the transition

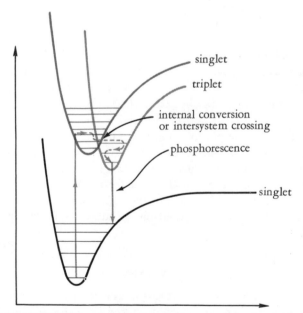

singlet

triplet

internal conversion
or intersystem crossing

phosphorescence

singlet

Figure 6–7 The arrangement of the potential-energy curves of excited states with different numbers of unpaired electrons so that phosphorescence can be observed.

probability is so low that few excited triplet-state molecules can be produced by such a mechanism.)

If excited singlet and triplet states exist with potential-energy curves like those shown in Fig. 6–7, there is an indirect mechanism whereby molecules can be put into the triplet state. The sample containing the molecules can be irradiated with radiation that raises the molecules to the high-energy singlet state. The molecules will then lose vibrational energy and the process of internal conversion might carry the molecule from the initial singlet excited state to the triplet state. It should be mentioned here that internal conversion between states with different numbers of unpaired electrons is sufficiently difficult compared to ordinary internal conversion that it is often given the special name *intersystem crossing*. If intersystem crossing does occur to an appreciable extent, further vibrational deactivation will move the molecule stepwise down the vibrational levels until it occupies the lowest vibrational level of the electronic configuration with two unpaired electrons.

Often, no rapid easy process is then available to the molecule. It resorts to the emission of radiation from the triplet state it occupies to a low-lying, or ground, singlet state. Thus, by the indirect process of excitation to a singlet state and internal conversion to a triplet state, the stage is set for phosphorescent emission.

The information obtained from the studies of phosphorescence, and fluorescence, is of great potential value in connection with studies of the nature of molecules in excited electronic states and of the mechanisms of chemical reactions. More particularly, chemical reactions that proceed as a result of the absorption of light, i.e., photochemical reactions, will be understandable only when the excited states, and the lifetimes of these states, are well understood. Studies of the emission of radiation is the most direct approach to this information.

SUMMARY

Although most spectroscopic studies make use of the absorption of radiation, further information on the behavior of molecules is obtained by considering the processes by which molecules rid themselves of excess energy and return to the normal, or ground, state.

Some processes that accomplish this involve the emission of radiation, while in other processes the excess energy is shared with neighboring or colliding molecules and is dissipated as heat. Investigation of the emission processes leads to the recognition of two types: fluorescence, which generally occurs very rapidly, and phosphorescence, which can persist long after formation of the excited molecules has ceased.

To understand the nature and behavior of molecules with high-energy electron arrangements, it is necessary to know not only about the electronic state itself but also how the molecule in that state interacts with neighboring molecules and how long it survives in the excited state under various conditions. In studies of photochemical processes, photosynthesis in plants, or the process by which the pigments in the eye provide us with visual stimuli, for example, this information on the excited state produced by the initial absorption of light is basic to a real understanding of the ensuing effects. Further work on the phosphorescence and fluorescence of chemical systems that are involved in important photochemical processes must yet be done for these processes to be completely understood.

Glossary: Symbols

Δ	Energy separation of the d electrons of a transition metal that results from the presence of coordinating groups.
10Dq	Equivalent to Δ.
$\Delta\epsilon$	The energy of a quantum of radiation, or the change in the energy of a molecule.
$\epsilon_{rot.}$	The energies of the allowed rotational states of a molecule.
$\epsilon_{vib.}$	The energies of the allowed vibrational states of a molecule.
f	The force acting on a particle or atom.
I	Moment of inertia. Defined as $I = \Sigma m_i r_i^2$ where m_i is the mass of the i-th particle and r_i is the distance of the i-th particle from the center of gravity.
J	The rotational quantum number. The allowed values of J are 0, 1, 2, ...
k	The force constant of a spring, usually reported in dynes per centimeter for a chemical bond *or* Boltzmann's constant.
l	The azimuthal quantum number for an electron of an

atom. This number determines the orbital angular momentum of an electron and the shape of the orbit it occupies.

λ   The wavelength of radiation ($\lambda = c/\nu$).

μ   The reduced mass of a diatomic molecule. If m_1 and m_2 are the masses of the two atoms of a diatomic molecule,

$$\mu = \frac{m_1 m_2}{m_1 + m_2}.$$

n The number of atoms in a molecule, *or* the principal quantum number for the electrons of an atom, *or* a symbol indicating that electrons of a molecule are nonbonding.

ω   The angular velocity of a rotating system expressed in radians per second.

ν Frequency in cycles per second ($\nu = c/\lambda$).

$\nu_{classical}$ The vibrational frequency of a system that is not subjected to quantum restrictions.

$\nu_{rot.}$ The rotational frequency; i.e., the number of revolutions per second of a rotating system.

$\bar{\nu}$ The wave number in reciprocal centimeters ($\bar{\nu} = 1/\lambda$).

r The distance from the center of rotation to a particle of the rotating system.

r_e The equilibrium length of a chemical bond; i.e., the length a bond would have if the molecule could have zero vibrational energy.

s,p,d . . .   Letters indicating that the quantum number l has the values 0,1,2, ...

v The vibrational quantum number. The allowed values of v are 0,1,2, . . . *or* the velocity of a particle.

x The displacement of a particle from its equilibrum position.

Index

Absorption band, 13
Absorption line, 13
Amplitude of molecular vibrations, 74, 75
Angstrom unit, 7
Angular momentum, 36
Angular velocity, 33
Antisymmetric vibration, 80, 81
Asymmetric top, 50, 96

Boltzmann's constant, 16
Boltzmann distribution, 24, 25, 98
Butadiene, 122

Centrifugal distortion, 54
Characteristic frequencies, 80, 81
Charge-transfer spectra, 133–136
Crystal field, 130–133
d electrons, 127–133
Degeneracy, 98
Degree of freedom, 17
Delocalization, 123
Dipole, 46
Dissociation energy, 114, 115

Electric field of radiation, 5
Electronic energy, 20, 21

Electronic spectra, due to nonbonding electrons, 123–126
of hydrocarbons, 118–123
of metal ions, 126–133
Electronic spectroscopy, 26, 106
Energies of molecules, 15–21
Ethylene, 120, 121

Fluorescence, 144–147
Force constant, 63, 64
table of, 74
Frequency of radiation, 6
Fundamental frequency, 73

Gas constant, 17

h, Planck's constant, 9
HBr, rotation-vibration spectrum, 93, 94
H_2O, rotation-vibration spectrum, 95, 96
Hooke's law, 63, 82, 83
Hydrocarbons, electronic spectra of, 118–123
I, moment of inertia, 34
I_2, absorption spectrum of, 112
Infrared region, 9, 10

Internal conversion, 143
Intersystem crossing, 150

J, rotational quantum number, 37

k, Boltzmann's constant, 16
k, force constant, 63, 64

Ligand, 129
Ligand field, 131–133

Magnetic field of radiation, 5
Microwave region, 9, 10
Moment of inertia, 34
μ, reduced mass, 35
Multiplicity, 98
Newton's laws of motion, 24
Nonbonding electrons, 125
Nonradiative processes, 139–144
$\nu_{classical}$, 65, 68
Nuclear rotations, 54, 55

Overtones, 84, 85

Phosphorescence, 148–150
π bond, 120
π^* state, 121
Planck, Max, 8, 9
Planck's constant, 9
Population, of rotational energy
    levels, 96–99
    of vibrational energy levels, 70
Potential energy, 75, 82–85, 110, 111

Quantum nature of radiation, 8, 9
Quantum numbers, 37
Quantum restrictions, 21–24

R, gas constant, 17
Radiation, 4–9
    quantum nature of, 8
    wave nature of, 4–8
Radiative processes, 139–150

Reduced mass, 36
    in rotational calculations, 36
    in vibrational calculations, 67
Rotational energy, 17, 18, 33–36
Rotational spectroscopy, 26
Rotation-vibration bands, 91–103
    asymmetry of, 99–103
    intensities in, 96–99
    shape of, 91–93

Schroedinger equation, 23, 24
Selection rule, 48
    for rotational-energy changes, 48
    for vibrational-energy changes, 76, 77
σ bonds, 121
Singlet state, 144
Spectrograph, 11
Spectrometer, 11, 12
Spectrophotometer, 11
Spectroscope, 11
Symmetric top, 50
Symmetric vibration, 80, 81

Transition metals, 127–133
Translational energy, 16, 17
Triplet state, 144

Ultraviolet region, 9, 10

Vibrational energy, 19, 20
    of diatomic molecules, 68–71
Vibrational spectroscopy, 26
Vibrations, classical, 62–68
    of diatomic molecules, 68–71
    quantum mechanical, 68–71
Visible region, 9, 10

Wavelength, 5, 6
Wave nature of radiation, 4–8

Zero-point energy, 69